VENOM

BIRTH OF A MONSTER

**PETER DAVID • RICHARD BUCKLER •
DAVID MICHELINIE • TODD MCFARLANE**

VENOM
BIRTH OF A MONSTER

CONTENTS

MARVEL POCKETBOOK Venom: Birth Of A Monster

Venom: Birth Of A Monster. Marvel Pocketbook Vol. 1. Contains material originally published in magazine form as Peter Parker, The Spectacular Spider-Man #107-110 & The Amazing Spider-Man (Vol. 1) #298-300. First printing 2007. Published by Panini Publishing, a division of Panini UK Limited. Office of publication: Panini House, Coach and Horses Passage, The Pantiles, Tunbridge Wells, Kent TN2 5UJ. Copyright © 1985, 1988 & 2007 Marvel Characters, Inc. All rights reserved. All characters featured in this edition and the distinctive names and likenesses thereof are trademarks of Marvel Characters, Inc. No similarity between any of the names, characters, persons and/or institutions in this edition with those of any living or dead person or institution is intended, and any such similarity which may exist is purely coincidental. This publication may not be sold, except by authorised dealers, and is sold subject to the condition that it shall not be sold or distributed with any part of its cover or markings removed, nor in a mutilated condition. This publication is produced under licence from Marvel Characters, Inc. through Panini S.p.A. Printed in Italy.
ISBN: 978-1-84653-052-4

"MY FATHER, THE MACHO POLICE INSPECTOR, NEVER FORGAVE MY MOTHER FOR SPAWNING A GIRL. THEY SPLIT FOR GOOD WHEN I WAS SIX MONTHS OLD."

"THE COURTS, SOLOMON-LIKE, SPLIT CUSTODY AS WELL. DAD GOT MY BIG BROTHER, BRIAN. MOM GOT ME."

"MOM WAS THRILLED. SHE HAD SWORN OFF MEN IN GENERAL AND COPS IN PARTICULAR."

"HER RESOLVE LASTED FOUR YEARS BEFORE SHE UPPED AND MARRIED PATROLMAN CARL WEATHERBY. MOM BECAME CELIA WEATHERBY, DROPPING HER OLD MARRIED NAME."

"I REMAINED DeWOLFF. JEAN DeWOLFF."

"I ADORED MY STEP-DAD, AND THE FEELING WAS MUTUAL. CARL LOVED BEING A COP. AND HE MADE ME LOVE IT, TOO."

"OF COURSE, HE NEVER TOLD ME ABOUT MOM'S LONG NIGHTS WHILE HE WAS OUT KEEPING THE CITY SAFE."

"I DON'T KNOW HOW SHE MANAGED TO LIVE WITH IT. JUMPING WHEN THE PHONE RANG. SHRINKING FROM A KNOCK AT THE DOOR."

"WAITING TO HEAR HER HUSBAND WAS DEAD."

"NO, I JUST HEARD ABOUT THE EXCITEMENT, THE BLUE KNIGHT IN ARMOR. AND WHEN I STARTED WEARING A LITTLE BADGE HE BROUGHT ME HOME, I THOUGHT MOM WOULD SHOOT HIM HERSELF."

"BUT WE ALL KNEW IT WAS INEVITABLE. AFTER ALL, MY VERY GENDER HAD LOST ME ANY APPROVAL FROM MY NATURAL FATHER. GETTING MY STEP-DAD'S APPROVAL WAS EVERYTHING TO ME NOW."

"DEEP DOWN, I SUPPOSE, I WANTED TO BE DADDY'S LITTLE GIRL."

"THE DAY I GRADUATED THE ACADEMY AND EARNED MY SHIELD, CARL DIDN'T CRACK A SMILE. YET I COULD TELL HE WAS FLYING, AS WAS I. MOM, NATURALLY, CRIED IN THE BATHROOM FOR TWO DAYS."

"DAD...CARL...KEPT PUSHING. AND I, CRAVING HIS APPROVAL, PUSHED JUST AS HARD."

"I SHOT THROUGH THE RANKS. I HAD A TRUNKFUL OF COMMENDATIONS WHEN I GOT MY CAPTAINCY."

"HE WAS STILL A SERGEANT. I THOUGHT HE'D HAVE A STROKE."

"INSTEAD, WHEN I TOLD HIM, HE STILL DIDN'T CRACK A SMILE. HE JUST NODDED. BUT I KNEW HE WAS PROUD. AND I ALSO KNEW THEN WHY HE DIDN'T SMILE MUCH AT MY ACHIEVEMENTS."

2

"HE WANTS ME TO BE THE FIRST WOMAN POLICE COMMISSIONER. AND HE KNOWS THE ONLY WAY TO GET THERE IS IF YOU'RE TOTALLY DRIVEN. SO HE'S WITHHOLDING THE SMILE UNTIL THAT DAY."

"I'LL GET THAT SMILE OUT OF HIM YET."

"WHAT'S THAT POUNDING? AT THE DOOR? IN MY HEAD?"

THUMP THUMP!

"I WONDER WHY I FEEL SO RELAXED?"

KRAK!

"AND I WONDER...WHY WAS I THINKING OF MY LIFE JUST NOW?"

≡URK!≡ THAT STENCH! THAT'S WHAT I WAS SMELLING. IT'S WHY I CALLED. WHAT...?

SHUT UP. GET BACK IN THE HALL.

CAPTAIN? CAPTAIN DeWOLFF?

AW NO.

RUSS! IN HERE. IT'S CAPTAIN DeWOLFF.

I THINK.

CALL IT IN. AND HAVE 'EM SEND PEOPLE WITH STRONG STOMACHS.

DON'T YOU READ THE *DAILY BUGLE* ? IF YOU *CAN* READ, THAT IS ?

IT'S RIGHT THERE, ABOUT HOW UNTRUST-WORTHY I AM. I'M AS BIG A MENACE AS YOU GUYS.

HOW ABOUT THAT ? THEY FELL ASLEEP ON ME.

THAT JUST LEAVES THEIR FRIEND. THE ONE WHO LIKES IT WHEN OLD MEN GRUNT.

≡GASP! GASP!≡

≡WHEEZE!≡

≡GASP!≡

HI THERE! SNUFF ANY CRIPPLES TODAY ?

YEEP!

ALL RIGHT! I GIVE UP! YOU GOT ME. JUST ... JUST UNCLENCH YOUR FIST, OKAY ?

YOU DON'T UNDERSTAND. I *REALLY* WANT TO CLEAN YOUR CLOCK FOR YOU. AND MY ANALYST SAID NOT TO REPRESS FRUSTRATION.

BUT ... BUT I'M *SURRENDERING.* YOU *CAN'T* HIT ME. YOU WOULDN'T DARE!

OH, I WAS *HOPING* YOU'D SAY THAT.

POW!

RADIO THE BACK-UP UNIT. I THINK WE FOUND THE THIRD PERPETRATOR.

WE APOLOGIZE FOR OUR APPEARANCE DUE TO CONSTRUCTION!

POLICE

SPLA CHUNK!

UH-OH. IT'S SPIDER-MAN. LET'S TAKE THIS SLOW, SARGE.

AT EASE, SANDY. I HAVE A FEELING THE WEB-SLINGER'S THE ONE WHO PUT OUT THE GARBAGE FOR US.

NO M-MORE...

MOMENTS LATER...

I WANT HIM ARRESTED! HE USED EXCESSIVE FORCE, AND HARMED ME GRIEVOUSLY, AND OTHER STUFF.

MOI!?

GEE, BAD BREAK. NO WITNESSES.

THAT'S LIFE IN THE BIG CITY, I GUESS.

SPIDER-MAN, DON'T RUN OFF! YOU'LL WANT TO KNOW ABOUT THE VICTIM ...

WE'VE ROUNDED UP THE OTHER TWO. THE VICTIM'S ON HIS WAY TO THE HOSPITAL TO CHECK FOR CONCUSSION, BUT HE LOOKS TO BE OKAY.

BY THE WAY, DID YOU HEAR ABOUT JEAN DEWOLFF?

IS THIS THE JOKE ABOUT JEAN AND THE MIAMI DOLPHINS? YEAH, I...

SHE'S DEAD. SOMEONE BLEW HER AWAY.

WHAT? YOU'RE KIDDING.

SHE'S REALLY DEAD? BUT...I JUST SAW HER THE OTHER DAY...

OH, CRUD.

WHO DID IT?

DON'T KNOW YET. WHO EVER DOES THIS KIND OF STUFF? SOME GODLESS SICKO.

10

[15]

FATHER?

FATHER--?

YES, MY SON? YOU SEEM TROUBLED.

FATHER, I'D LIKE TO TAKE CONFESSION.

CERTAINLY, MY SON. THE CONFESSIONAL IS OVER THIS WAY.

AND PRESENTLY, WITHIN THE CONFINES OF THE CONFESSIONAL BOOTH, OBSCURED FROM THE PRIEST BY A SCREEN ...

BLESS ME, FATHER, FOR I HAVE SINNED. IT HAS BEEN THREE WEEKS SINCE MY LAST CON- FESSION.

IN THAT TIME I HAVE COMMITTED...

COLD BLOODED MURDER, ROBBIE.

NO MATTER HOW LONG I PUBLISH THE BUGLE, I'LL NEVER GET USED TO HEAD- LINES LIKE THIS.

IT'S NOT EASY FOR US EDITORS EITHER, JONAH.

A FINE OFFICER LIKE JEAN DeWOLFF, MURDERED IN HER BED.

I ALWAYS THOUGHT YOU SAID YOU DIDN'T LIKE HER. THE CHARM OF AN ICE CUBE TRAY, YOU SAID.

FOR PITY'S SAKE, ROBBIE, I DIDN'T LIKE JFK EITHER. THAT DOESN'T MEAN SOME- ONE I DON'T LIKE DESERVES TO GET KILLED.

WHAT ABOUT SPIDER- MAN? WHAT IF HE WERE KILLED, FIGHT- ING THOSE CRIMINALS YOU ALWAYS CLAIM HE'S IN CAHOOTS WITH?

YOU'RE BEING BLASTED MORBID, ROBBIE.

IT'S A MORBID NEWSDAY, JONAH. WELL?

WELL... HITLER DESERVED TO DIE...

AND SO DO ASSASSINS AND COP KILLERS. SCUM LIKE THAT. WHATEVER ELSE HE IS, SPIDER-MAN IS *NOT* ONE OF THOSE.

WHY JONAH, THAT'S THE NICEST THING YOU'VE EVER SAID ABOUT SPIDER-MAN IN YOUR LIFE.

YEAH, BUT DON'T QUOTE ME.

MR. ROBERTSON? AH... SORRY TO BREAK IN. I'M REVEREND JACKSON TOLLIVER.

HELLO, REVEREND. I'M J. JONAH JAMESON, THE BUGLE'S PUBLISHER.

YES. SO, MR. ROBERTSON, I'M SETTING UP A MINISTRY IN NEW YORK AND I WAS HOPING TO GET SOME MENTION IN YOUR PAPER.

TOLLIVER... WEREN'T YOU MENTIONED PROMINENTLY IN THE ATLANTA SLAYINGS SEVERAL YEARS AGO?

WHY, I'M SURPRISED, SIR, THAT A WHITE MAN WOULD CARE SO MUCH ABOUT THE SLAYINGS OF YOUNG BLACK CHILDREN.

WHY, REVEREND TOLLIVER... ARE YOU A RACIST?

MY APOLOGIES, SIR.

I'VE LIVED THROUGH SOME RATHER RARIFIED TIMES, AND PERHAPS I HAVE A HABIT OF GOING INTO ANY SITUATION WITH A CHIP ON MY SHOULDER.

AN UNFORTUNATE TENDENCY, INDEED...

FOR A MAN OF GOD.

12

EARLY EVENING...

POLICE DEPT.

ANYBODY SEE CHRIS AND MARY BETH? THEY'RE ON COFFEE CLEAN-UP THIS WEEK.

THEY'RE NOT OUT HERE.

HI. I'D LIKE TO TALK TO WHOEVER IS IN CHARGE OF THE JEAN DEWOLFF KILLING.

THAT'S SERGEANT STAN CARTER, BUT HE JUST WENT OFF SHIFT.

HE DRIVES A RED CAPRICE CLASSIC-- IF YOU HURRY YOU CAN STILL CATCH HIM.

MUCH OBLIGED.

WOW, HE SOUNDED BARELY HOSTILE. MAYBE THEY WANT ALL THE HELP ON POOR JEAN'S MURDER THEY CAN GET.

AH, THERE WE GO. THAT LOOKS LIKELY.

I'LL TRY NOT TO STARTLE HIM. WOULDN'T WANT AN ACCIDENT ON MY CONSCIENCE.

HI THERE! YOU DETECTIVE CARTER?

WHO WANTS TO KNOW?

13

YOU PLANNING ON STAYING UP THERE? OR MAYBE YOU'RE JUST ANSWERING MY AD FOR A HOOD ORNAMENT? EITHER WAY, CHATTING WITH COPS ISN'T YOUR USUAL STYLE.

I KNOW. BUT I WANTED TO TALK ABOUT THE JEAN DEWOLFF KILLING.

WHY? YOU DO IT?

YOU ASK A *LOT* OF QUESTIONS.

HOW ELSE DO I GET ANSWERS, KIDDO?

SO WHAT, YOU WANT AN ENGRAVED INVITATION? GET IN ALREADY.

HONK! HONK!

SMELLS GOOD... COFFEE?

HOT COCOA. WANT SOME?

SURE.

TOO BAD. THIS IS ALL I'VE GOT. SO... YOU WANNA PLAY DETECTIVE?

NOT ME. I CAN'T EVEN HANDLE COLONEL MUSTARD IN THE PARLOR WITH THE CANDLESTICK. BUT I'D LIKE TO KNOW HOW IT HAPPENED.

ABRUPTLY, JEAN WAS SHOT IN THE UPPER RIGHT CHEST WITH A DOUBLE-BARRELLED SHOTGUN. FIRED AT CLOSE RANGE. TOOK OUT MOST OF HER TORSO.

THE CLOSENESS COMBINED WITH A NEIGHBOR'S NOISY STEREO SERVED TO STIFLE THE NOISE CONSIDERABLY.

AND HERE'S SOMETHING WEIRD-- HER BADGE WAS MISSING.

NO PARKING 8 to 6 pm

ANY SUSPECTS?

ABOUT TEN MILLION, COUNTING YOU. AND ME.

DETOUR SOUTH STREET

YOU STILL THINK I DID IT?

A GOOD COP EYES EVERYONE WITH SUSPICION. EVEN NORMAL CITIZENS SUCH AS YOURSELF.

OOOO—KAY. ONE POINT FOR YOU.

ACTUALLY, COSTUMED FOLKS LIKE YOU DON'T CONCERN ME ALL THAT MUCH. OBVIOUS NUTS I DON'T WORRY ABOUT.

IT'S THE QUIET, UNOBVIOUS NUTS THAT YOU HAVE TO WATCH.

YOU'RE RIGHT. ON THE NEWS NEIGHBORS ALWAYS SAY, "HE WAS SO NICE. I CAN'T BELIEVE HE CHOPPED THOSE GIRL SCOUTS INTO COOKIES."

YOU KNOW, THAT COCOA SMELLS REAL GOOD.

MINUTES LATER...

WHY WERE YOU GIVEN THIS CASE, STAN?

THE WHOLE FORCE WAS GIVEN THE CASE. I'M JUST THE COORDINATOR. BUT WE ALL HAVE A STAKE IN THIS.

WE LIKED JEAN AND, THOUGH SHE TRIED NOT TO SHOW IT, SHE LIKED US. SHE RARELY SMILED, YOU KNOW.

A SHAME, A WOMAN THAT STRIKING NEVER SMILING. SHE EVEN LIKED YOU, WEB-SLINGER, WHICH IS PARTLY WHY I'M TALKING WITH YOU. SHE SPOKE VERY HIGHLY OF YOU.

REALLY? YOU KNOW... THERE WAS ALWAYS SOMETHING ABOUT HER THAT...

OH HECK. I SUPPOSE IT'S WHY I'M HERE. YOU SEE...

I LIKED HER TOO.

"MAN WITHOUT FEAR." WHAT A LAUGH.

IF I COULD SEE WHAT I'M DOING...

I'D BE SCARED STIFF.

UH OH. I DON'T NEED HYPER-SENSITIVE HEARING TO KNOW...

THAT THE WMJD TRAFFIC COPTER IS TAKING OFF ALREADY.

WELL I'M NOT GOING TO MISS MY LIFT. NOT WHILE I'VE GOT MY BILLY CLUB...

I'VE GOT TO START GETTING UP EARLIER.

SNAGGED IT! NOW ALL I HAVE TO DO IS RE-TRACT MY CABLE, AND HOPE I GO UP INSTEAD OF THE 'COPTER COMING DOWN.

SECONDS LATER...

WELL ...

...IT BEATS THE SUBWAY. AFTER ALL...

WITH THOSE MUGGERS AND DERAILINGS AND FIRES, THE SUBWAY'S A GOOD PLACE TO GET KILLED.

A MAN OF MANY FACES...

THIS IS ANOTHER FACE OF MATT MURDOCK ON VIEW SOMETIME LATER AT MANHATTAN CRIMINAL COURTS.

AS AN ATTORNEY, MATT OCCASIONALLY DONATES HIS TIME TO HELPING OUT THE OVERWORKED PUBLIC DEFENDERS OFFICE.

SUCH WORK IS CALLED *PRO BONO PUBLICA*... "FOR THE PUBLIC GOOD." BUT THERE ARE SOME IN THE AUDIENCE THIS DAY WHO WOULD ARGUE...

... THAT THE PUBLIC'S GOOD IS NOT ABOUT TO BE SERVED.

NO, YOUR HONOR. I FEEL $500 BAIL FOR EACH OF MY CLIENTS IS EXCESSIVE.

I REMIND YOU THIS IS MY CLIENTS' FIRST OFFENSE...

FIRST TIME THEY WERE CAUGHT, HE MEANS.

AND THEY ARE INDIGENT. ANY BAIL AMOUNT GUARANTEES JAIL TIME FOR THREE YOUNG MEN WITH SPOTLESS RECORDS.

COUNSELOR, YOU SEEM TO THINK YOU'RE REPRE-SENTING THREE APOSTLES.

I'M NOT RE-QUEST-ING CANON-IZATION, YOUR HONOR...

...MERELY AN ASSUMPTION OF INNO-CENCE.

THANK YOU, COUNSELORS. DEFENDANTS ARE RELEASED ON THEIR OWN RE-COGNISANCE.

COUNSELOR, INSTRUCT YOUR CLIENTS TO RESTRAIN THEM-SELVES...

...AND REMIND THEM THAT FAILURE TO SHOW UP FOR THEIR COURT DATE WILL RESULT IN EXTREMELY UNPLEASANT PENALTIES.

ONE HOUR RELEASE FOR LUNCH.

SEE? I TOLD'JA IF WE STUCK TOGETHER WITH ONE LAWYER WE'D DO GOOD.

18

THAT--THAT'S *IT?* BUT I DIDN'T SAY HOW THEY KNOCKED ME DOWN. HOW...

IT'S AN ARRAIGNMENT, ERNIE. NOT THE TRIAL.

INCREDIBLE. MATT MURDOCK, HOT-SHOT LAWYER, HELP-ING SCUM LIKE THAT GO FREE.

SEE YA IN THE FUNNY PAPERS, POPS.

AND DON'T STAY OUT LATE.

YOU DON'T COME WITHIN A MILE OF HIM, GOT THAT?

MURDOCK! STAY RIGHT THERE!

IT'S GUYS LIKE YOU WHO KEEP THINGS SAFE FOR SLIME. HOW CAN YOU FACE YOURSELF IN THE MIRROR EACH MORNING?

THAT HEARTBEAT... VOICE... IT'S *SPIDER-MAN.* BUT HE MUST BE IN HIS CIVVIES.

IT'S A CHALLENGE.

PETER PARKER! SHAME ON YOU!!

OH. THE BLIND THING. UH...

SORRY.

THE IDEA--!

OKAY! I APOLOGIZED, DIDN'T I? ALTHOUGH, FRANKLY...

I THINK MURDOCK SHOULD BE DOING THE APOLOGIZING.

YOU KNOW, HORACE, BACK IN COLLEGE YOU IMPRESSED ON STUDENTS LIKE ME THAT EVERYONE HAD TO BE TREATED EQUALLY UNDER THE LAW.

THAT EVERYONE DESERVES THE BEST EFFORTS WE CAN GIVE, DEFENDANT AS WELL AS PLAINTIFF.

AND I BELIEVE THAT. I DO.

SO WHY DO I FEEL LIKE TWENTY POUNDS OF BROILED INNER TUBE?

19

BECAUSE YOU DON'T LIKE YOUR CURRENT CLIENTS VERY MUCH, MATTHEW. YOU HATE GETTING YOUR HANDS DIRTY.

UNTRUE, HORACE.

TOO TRUE, MATT.

YOU SHOULD BE A PUBLIC DEFENDER FOR A FEW YEARS. IT'D STRENGTHEN YOUR RESOLVE.

GIVE YOU SOME GUTS.

LET ME HAVE A MINUTE TO USE THE LITTLE JUDGE'S ROOM, AND THEN WE'LL GRAB SOME LUNCH.

UH... FINE.

GOOD, HORACE, MAKE A CONVENIENT EXIT...

...SO I CAN CHECK OUT JUST WHO MY RADAR SENSE HAS DETECTED IN YOUR STUDY.

IF IT WEREN'T FOR HORACE, I'D CHANGE TO DD. AS IT IS...

...I MIGHT NOT HAVE THE TIME.

ONE PERSON... BULKY, MALE. HOLDING A LONG, THIN OBJECT...

A SHOT-GUN.

HIS PULSE IS RACING WILDLY. PERSPIRATION SO THICK... I THINK HE'S ON DRUGS.

WHO'S THERE? WHO IS IT?

I AM THE SIN-EATER. AND YOU ARE--?

HIS VOICE--! HIS AURA IS LIKE DECAYING VERMIN.

DON'T HURT ME. I'M BLIND.

20

PETER DAVID
Writer

RICH BUCKLER
Penciler

BRETT BREEDING
Inker

PHIL FELIX
Letterer

BOB SHAREN
Colorist

JIM OWSLEY
Editor

JIM SHOOTER
Editor In Chief

YOUR HONOR? *JUDGE ROSENTHAL,* SIR?

I JUST WANTED TO THANK YOU FOR COMING TO LECTURE IN OUR CLASS TODAY.

REALLY? IS THAT ALL? YOU APPEAR TO HAVE A BONE TO PICK.

NO SIR. *YES* SIR. I THINK YOUR DECISION ON THE BERRINGER CASE WAS COMPLETELY WRONG, SIR.

IS THAT A FACT?

THEN WHY WAIT UNTIL CLASS WAS *OVER* TO SAY SO? DON'T ANSWER...

IT'S BECAUSE YOU YOUNG LAW STUDENTS HAVEN'T ENOUGH *GUTS, THAT'S* WHY.

AFRAID TO SPEAK YOUR *MIND.* AFRAID TO DO WHAT YOU *HAVE* TO DO--

--WHAT YOU *SHOULD* DO, TO REMAIN *TRUE* TO YOURSELF.

IF YOU DON'T BELIEVE IN *YOURSELF,* THEN THE REST OF YOUR LIFE IS *HOLLOW. NOTHING* MATTERS EXCEPT WHAT YOU BELIEVE IN.

SO...WHAT WAS MY "ERROR", MR...?

MURDOCK. MATT MURDOCK.

SOMEONE SHOT A *JUDGE!*

PUBLIC SERVICE IF YA ASK *ME.*

NOBODY *DID,* YOU SLIME!

OH *YEAH,* BIG SHOT? DITCH THE *GLASSES* AND SAY THAT!

HE'S *BLIND,* YOU IDIOT!

FIGURES. ONLY WITNESS IS BLIND.

I'LL *GET* HIM, HORACE. I SWEAR...

I'LL *GET* HIM!

AND DO WHAT? SLUG 'IM WITH YOUR *CANE?*

WHOA! SLOW DOWN, MISTER!

MEN'S ROOM. CAN'T WAIT. *YOU* KNOW HOW IT IS!

THAT MASKED MANIAC, SIN-EATER, WENT OUT THE WINDOW RIGHT AFTER SHOOTING POOR HORACE...

"...BUT HE *WON'T* GET AWAY. *HE* DOESN'T KNOW WHAT *I* KNOW...THAT *I'M* COMING AFTER HIM AS *DAREDEVIL*

"...AND THAT *SPIDER-MAN* IS SOMEWHERE IN THE AREA TOO."

DAILY BUGLE

VIGILANTE STRIKES AGAIN

IT'S JUST *INSANE.* I TELL YOU MAY, PETER...

...I CAN'T *BELIEVE* THAT JUDGE LET THOSE PUNKS WHO MUGGED ME GO WITHOUT BAIL.

THIS IS *NO* WAY TO TREAT A VETERAN. I WAS *WOUNDED* FOR MY COUNTRY...

I EVEN STILL HAVE THE GUN I TOOK OFF A GERMAN SOLDIER.

I THINK ONE OF THOSE THREE PUNKS WAS GERMAN.

MAYBE THAT JUDGE WAS A *NAZI* SYMPATHIZER! YOU THINK *MAYBE--?*

JUDGE *ROSENTHAL?* DOESN'T SOUND LIKELY, MR. P.

IN THAT CASE I JUST *DON'T* UNDERSTAND! I TELL YOU, IF THIS KEEPS UP THE STREETS WON'T BE *SAFE* ANYMORE.

IRT

3

WHA-- YOU'RE STILL *CONSCIOUS?*

YEAH. 'CAUSE I *DO* KNOW A FEW THINGS...

LIKE HOW TO ROLL WITH PUNCHES--

--AND HOW TO *SUCKER* YOU INTO LETTING ME IN *CLOSE*...

SO I CAN DO *THIS!*

KRUNK!

GET HIM, SPIDEY! *KILL* HIM! *DON'T* STOP!

GET HIM!

I LOVE A MOB. THE ONLY THING YOU CAN *COUNT* ON...

...IS THAT YOU CAN'T *COUNT* ON THEM.

HAD *ENOUGH,* SLUGGER? OR DO I HAVE TO *BRUISE* ANOTHER KN-- *WAIT!*

NEXT TO THE *GAVEL* ON YOUR BELT-- A *BADGE!* YOU--

STAN TOLD ME JEAN'S *BADGE* WAS MISSING. YOU KILLED *JEAN DeWOLFF!*

YES. I *KILLED* HER.

AND A *JUDGE.*

AND NOW YOU!

WHAM!

UNNNNHH

SIGHT OF THE BADGE--WASN'T EXPECTING IT. CAUGHT ME OFF GUARD.

GOTTA PULL MYSELF TOGETHER...

JEAN...

NO! MUSTN'T THINK. JUST... REACT...

HE...KEEPS COMING... JUST NEED... A SECOND...

THAT TASTE IN... MY MOUTH...

BLEEDING, SINNER?

THE SIN-EATER HAS BROUGHT BLOOD TO ANOTHER SINNER. PRAISE THE LORD!

YOU THINK MY JOB'S EASY? BEING RESPONSIBLE FOR THE SINNERS?

IT'S NOT!

8

MY JOB IS IM-POSSIBLE! NEVER-ENDING!

NO. YOUR JOB IS FIN-ISHED, NOW!

HE'S GETTING *UP* AGAIN! HOW STRONG *IS* THIS GUY?

WAIT! OVER THERE IN THE CROWD...

WHAM!

AND SO ARE *YOU!*

AUNT MAY! WAS SHE HIT, OR...

HOLD IT, HAIRBALL! WHERE DO YOU THINK *YOU'RE* GOING?

ME? I ABSORB THE WORLD'S *SINS,* CRETIN. I'M GOING TO *HADES!*

I'LL SEE YOU THERE!

OHHHH NO YOU DON'T. NOT WHILE I'VE GOT MY *WEBS--*

NO WEBS. SWELL! HE MUST HAVE TRASHED MY SHOOTERS WITH THAT *GUN!*

9

NOW WHAT? I COULD GO AFTER HIM, SAVE FUTURE POSSIBLE VICTIMS.

BUT AUNT MAY MIGHT BE HURT, DYING! I CAN'T FAIL HER, LIKE I DID UNCLE BEN...

I HAVE TO STOP HIM. WHAT OTHER CHOICE DO I HAVE? BUT AUNT MAY...

WAIT! I DO HAVE ANOTHER CHOICE. IF I CAN TAG HIM WITH A SPIDER-TRACER...

PLEASE, LET JUST ONE THING GO RIGHT! PLEASE!

HMMM?

NO WAY, SINNER! NO WAY!

MOMENTS LATER...

ARE YOU CERTAIN YOU'RE ALL RIGHT, MAY?

STOP FUSSING OVER ME, ERNIE! HONESTLY! A FEW FRIGHTENED SOULS KNOCKED ME DOWN, IS ALL!

THE ONE I'M WORRIED ABOUT IS PETER. WHERE COULD HE HAVE GONE?

AUNT MAY! THANK HEAVENS YOU'RE OKAY!

I SAW YOU ON THE GROUND, AND I THOUGHT--

THOUGHT? YOU DIDN'T THINK. IF YOU HAD YOU'D NEVER HAVE LEFT YOUR AUNT'S SIDE!

HUSH ERNIE! IT'S NOT HIS FAULT!

10

MEANTIME, NEARBY...

THE COURTS BUILDING WAS A *MADHOUSE*. I THOUGHT I'D *NEVER* FIND SOMEPLACE TO CHANGE.

EXCEPT... *NOW* WHAT?

YOU'RE *TOO LATE*, DAREDEVIL. YOU MISSED THE WHOLE THING.

NO! SPIDER-MAN MUST HAVE TRIED TO STOP HIM-- AND *FAILED!*

BUT AT LEAST HE WAS HERE TO *TRY.*

I WAS TOO BUSY PROTECTING MY PRECIOUS IDENTITY. SO WHILE I WAS LOOKING FOR AN EMPTY ROOM TO *CHANGE* IN--

--SIN-EATER GOT CLEAN AWAY.

IF ONLY I COULD PICK UP ON THAT ERRATIC *HEARTBEAT* OF HIS. BUT THERE'S TOO MUCH NOISE AND CONFUSION.

NOT EVEN *MY* HYPERSENSES CAN CUT THROUGH IT ALL.

COP SHOT
$ 10,000 REWARD
OFFERED BY THE DAILY BUGLE

THIS IS ONE TIME I'D *KILL* TO BE SIGHTED. I DON'T KNOW WHAT SIN-EATER LOOKS LIKE.

"HE COULD BE A BLOCK AWAY WATCHING ME, AND I WOULDN'T EVEN KNOW."

11

NEXT DAY...

STAN, WE GOTTA TALK!

PIPE DOWN!

NO, NOT *YOU*. I'VE BEEN WAITING FOR THIS BALLISTICS REPORT *TOO LONG* TO WANT YOU TO QUIET DOWN.

IT'S *DEFINITE*, THEN? THE WEAPON THAT KILLED THE JUDGE YESTERDAY WAS THE SAME ONE USED TO KILL JEAN.

FANCY THAT.

THANKS, FRANK. GOTTA GO... *SPIDER-MAN'S* WAITING TO TALK TO ME.

YEAH, I'M A PISTOL. I KNOW.

I CAN VERIFY THIS "SIN-EATER'S" OUR MAN.

OH, CAN *YOU*, OFFICER?

YEAH. HE HAD JEAN'S *BADGE* ON HIS BELT. RIGHT NEXT TO THE JUDGE'S GAVEL. YOU MENTIONED IN THE CAR THE OTHER NIGHT THAT JEAN'S SHIELD WAS MISSING FROM HER APARTMENT. *

SHIELD, HUH? PICKING UP OUR LINGO, ARE YOU?

PICK UP A *BLACK EYE* UNDER THAT MASK, TOO? WORD IS HE GAVE YOU A REAL TUSSEL.

SPLIT LIP. IT'S FINE NOW. I HEAL FAST.

* *LAST ISSUE -- OWZ.*

12

WELL, IN SOME SUPER-STITIOUS SOCIETIES, LIKE IN THE OZARKS, THEY LEAVE THEIR RECENTLY DECEASED LAID OUT WITH FRUITS OR EDIBLES ON THEIR CHESTS.

EXCEPT *OUR* GUY IS *KILLING* PEOPLE... AND THEN TAKES TOKENS OF HIS VICTIMS' AUTHORITY WITH HIM, SINCE THE ITEMS WOULD BE ASSOCIATED WITH THE "SINS."

THAT'S *SICK*.

AND A MAN COMES WHOSE *ONLY* JOB IN LIFE IS TO EAT THOSE FRUITS, WHICH REPRESENT THE SINS OF THE DECEASED.

ONCE HE EATS THEM, THE DECEASED SOUL IS *CLEANSED*, READY FOR HEAVEN, COURTESY OF THE *SIN-EATER.*

SAY NOW. SOME GUYS HAVE THEIR *WIFE'S* PICTURE ON THEIR DESKS...

...*YOU'VE* GOT *NICK FURY*, THE HEAD OF *SHIELD.*

I WASN'T ALWAYS A SIMPLE *FLATFOOT*, SPIDER-MAN. YOU SEE BEFORE YOU A FORMER AGENT OF *SHIELD.*

BEST WISHES, NICK FURY

A STORY I *MAY* BORE YOU WITH IF YOU DON'T COME TO THE POINT OF YOUR VISIT.

I WANT TO CHECK OUT JEAN'S APARTMENT... THROUGH OFFICIAL CHANNELS, JUST TO PROVE MY SINCERITY.

THOUGH MY SPIDER SENSE DOESN'T *USUALLY* WORK THAT WAY...

STILL, I WANT TO SEE IF I CAN USE IT TO DETECT SOMETHING YOU GUYS *MISSED.*

FORGET IT.'

DO YOU *KNOW* HOW MANY DIRTY LOOKS I GET JUST FROM TALKING TO YOU? I HAVE *FEW* ENOUGH FRIENDS ON THE FORCE AS IT IS.

WHAT DOES YOUR *PARTNER* SAY ABOUT ALL THIS?

NOT MUCH. HE WAS KILLED SIX MONTHS AGO.

OH, HEY... I'M SORRY.

ME TOO. I GOT THE PUNKS WHO DID IT, BUT IT WON'T BRING HIM BACK.

14

LOOK, FELLA, MY AUTHORITY ONLY GOES SO FAR. BESIDES, THE APARTMENT IS SEALED.

OF COURSE, IT'S FUNNY ABOUT SEALS ...

THEY CAN BE *BROKEN.*

I DIDN'T HEAR YOU *SAY* THAT.

YOU KNOW THE *ADDRESS?*

MEANTIME...

YES ?

DO YOU WISH TO--?

UHM, YEAH. B-BLESS ME ...

BLESS ME FATHER FOR I HAVE *SINNED.*

I...I WAS HERE THE OTHER DAY, FATHER.

I STILL HEAR THE *VOICES,* FATHER... VOICES IN THE NIGHT ...

15

"AND THEY *SAY* TERRIBLE THINGS..."

STAN CARTER'S A REALLY DECENT GUY FOR A COP. THE MOST DECENT SINCE...

SINCE *JEAN*, I GUESS.

THERE WAS ALWAYS SOMETHING ABOUT HER-- AS IF SHE KEPT HERSELF *REINED IN* TOO TIGHT.

HERE'S HER PLACE.

UH BOY.

SHE PUT UP A FIGHT... EITHER THAT OR SIN-EATER SIMPLY *WRECKED* THE PLACE.

OKAY, SPIDEY-SENSE. TINGLE. *BUZZ*. HELP ME FIND SOME SMALL CLUE THE COPS MAY HAVE MISSED.

LIKE SIN-EATER'S *DRIVER'S LICENSE.*

C'MON, ALREADY. IT'S BEEN *TEN MINUTES.* GIVE ME *SOME* HINT THAT THERE'S SOMETHING USEFUL HERE.

FINALLY...

NOTHING. IF THERE'S SOME UNSEEN CLUE, IT'S *STAYING* UNSEEN.

I WAS HOPING FOR ONCE TO GET MY SPIDER-SENSE TO REACT TO SOMETHING OTHER THAN DANGER.

AFTER ALL, IT IS A KIND OF *ESP.* STILL, IT WAS A LONGSHOT AT BEST. THINK I'LL CHECK OUT THE DRESSER DRAWERS.

16

WONDER WHO THIS *COUPLE* IS? MUST BE JEAN'S FOLKS.

HERE'S AN ENVELOPE STUFFED TO THE *BRIM!* WHAT IS ...

I ... DON'T *BELIEVE* IT.

THEY'RE ALL OF *ME!* EVERY LAST ONE!

I HAVEN'T SEEN SO MANY CLIPPINGS SINCE THAT DYING LITTLE BOY'S COLLECTION.

THIS ONE HAD THE CAT AND ME... BUT THE CAT'S CLIPPED OUT.

BUT WHY? WAS SHE DOING SOME SORT OF STUDY ON ME?

NO, SHE WOULD HAVE KEPT THAT AT HER OFFICE.

SHE KEPT THESE BECAUSE SHE LIKED THEM.

BUT... SHE NEVER SAID ANYTHING PARTICULARLY WARM TO ME. HECK, SHE USUALLY CHEWED ME *OUT*.

IT *CAN'T* BE. SHE *COULDN'T* HAVE CARED FOR ME.

WHY DIDN'T SHE EVER SAY ANYTHING IF SHE FELT ... AND MAYBE I WOULD HAVE ...

WE COULD HAVE...

IT *CAN'T* BE TRUE. SHE WAS ALWAYS SO COOL, SO ALOOF!

BLAST IT, WHY DID SHE HAVE TO BE THAT WAY?

"WHY?"

YOU MAY WELL ASK *WHY* JEAN DEWOLFF WAS *TAKEN* FROM US IN SUCH AN UNHAPPY AND UNTIMELY MANNER.

I *CANNOT* ANSWER THAT. ONLY OUR *LORD* KNOWS THE REASONS FOR THE HARDSHIPS THAT PLAGUE US...

AND ALTHOUGH I *MYSELF* NEVER HAD THE PRIVILEGE OF MEETING CAPTAIN DEWOLFF...

...I CAN SEE THAT SHE HAD MANY FRIENDS ON THIS EARTH. I MOURN WITH YOU, MY FRIENDS...

AND BELIEVE, WITH YOU, THAT GOD HAS GATHERED HER UP TO A *HAPPIER* PLACE WHERE SHE WILL KNOW *NO* VIOLENCE.

ASHES TO ASHES, DUST TO DUST.

DARLING...

DARLING, I...

DON'T YOU *TOUCH* ME! DON'T YOU *EVER* TOUCH ME *AGAIN!* IT'S YOUR FAULT!

WHO IN...?

JEAN'S FOLKS.

OH.

WHILE, NEARBY...

IT'S ODD...

COFFINS ARE ALWAYS SO SMALL. IT'S HARD TO BELIEVE HORACE IS *IN* THERE.

HE'S NOT REALLY. NOT THE HORACE *I* REMEMBER.

BIG. ROBUST. FULL OF LIFE.

FUNNY. HE ALWAYS SAID CIGARS WOULD BE THE DEATH OF HIM. WHO WOULD HAVE THOUGHT.

THAT OTHER FUNERAL'S BREAKING UP, TOO. WHAT A CHEERFUL D--

WAIT! WHAT AM I PICKING UP?

THE HEARTBEAT IS SLOWER BUT... IT'S *HIM!* I KNOW IT! THE *SIN-EATER!*

I LET YOU DOWN LAST TIME, HORACE, BUT NOT AGAIN. THIS TIME, SECRET OR NO, I'LL GET HIM!

19

BUT... WHICH ONE IS HE? TOO MANY PEOPLE TO PIN DOWN!

I COULD SHOUT OUT HE'S HERE, BUT HOW CAN I CONVINCE ANYONE?

AND HOW CAN I TESTIFY THAT I RECOGNIZE A HEARTBEAT!? THE D.A. WOULDN'T TOUCH IT! AND...

NERVOUS ABOUT BEING LEFT TO MIND THE STORE ALONE, ROBBIE.

I'LL WATCH OUT FOR YOUR PAPER, AND MARLA, JONAH. NO NEED TO WORRY.

WORRY? WITH NED AND I FLYING DOWN TO THE DISTRIBUTOR MEETING IN FLORIDA THIS EVENING...

MY MAIN WORRY IS THAT YOU'LL STOW AWAY IN MY LUGGAGE!

NOW THERE'S A THOUGHT.

YES, MISS MERCADO, MY TIME IN ATLANTA PROVES THAT POLICE CANNOT HANDLE THE SIMPLEST OF INVESTIGATIONS. NOTHING IS SOLVED UNLESS THE ANSWER IS DROPPED INTO THEIR LAPS.

FURTHERMORE, WHEN THE VICTIMS ARE BLACK, PARTICULARLY LOWER INCOME, YOU CAN FORGET ANY POLICE ATTENTION AT ALL.

SO THAT'S REVEREND JACKSON TOLLIVER. A FRIEND OF MINE IN THE ATLANTA P.D., HERB, SAID HE WAS HEADING OUR WAY.

I WONDER IF THE SIN-EATER DOES REQUESTS?

BAD JOKE, STAN. VERY BAD JOKE.

LAUGH SO YOU DON'T CRY, ARNIE.

THIS IS *IT!* I CAN'T *WAIT* ANY LONGER. I'VE GOT TO DO WHAT'S RIGHT.

WAIT! EVERYONE COME BACK! THE KILLER'S *HERE!*

WE'VE GOT TO STOP HIM BEFORE IT'S ...

...TOO LATE.

I'M GLAD WE'RE HAVING THIS CHANCE TO DISCUSS "NOW" PARKER.

BUT BEFORE WE *DO*, I'D LIKE TO SAY I'D APPRECIATE IT IF YOU COULD WATCH OUT FOR MY WIFE. I DON'T LIKE HAVING TO LEAVE MARLA...

THIS SIN-EATER HAS ME WORRIED...

DON'T *WORRY,* JONAH...

'CAUSE I'M NAILIN' THIS CREEP *MYSELF* WITHIN 48 HOURS.

JEAN, WHEREVER YOU ARE, I'LL GET HIM FOR YOU. I DON'T CARE *WHAT* I HAVE TO DO.

BECAUSE *I* LET HIM GET AWAY, AND I SWEAR THERE'LL BE NO FURTHER DEATHS AT HIS HANDS. *NONE.*

SOMETIME LATER...

THERE IS A PRIEST WITH A GREAT WEIGHT ON HIS SHOULDERS...

THAT WEIGHT WILL NOW BE REMOVED.

YES? DO YOU WISH TO TAKE CONFESSION?

FATHER, I...I HAVE A VERY DIFFICULT *TASK* AHEAD OF ME.

I HAVE CHOSEN A MISSION IN LIFE, THOUGH SOMETIMES I THINK *IT* HAS CHOSEN *ME.*

NOW I FIND MYSELF *WAVERING* IN MY COURSE. I NEED *ADVICE*, FATHER.

WHAT IS THE NATURE OF YOUR WORK, MY SON?

RIGHTING WRONGS, FATHER. WRONGS DONE BY IMPORTANT PEOPLE, IN IMPORTANT PLACES, THAT ONLY I CAN SEE.

BUT I'M AFRAID NO ONE WILL UNDERSTAND.

MY SON, YOU MUST ALWAYS DO WHAT YOU BELIEVE TO BE RIGHT. YOU MUST BE TRUE TO YOURSELF AND YOUR BELIEFS.

OUR SAVIOR TAUGHT US THE IMPORTANCE OF THIS. OF COURSE, WE ALSO KNOW YOU MUST SOMETIMES PAY A HEAVY PRICE FOR YOUR BELIEFS.

BUT IF YOU *TRULY* BELIEVE IN YOUR CAUSE, THEN YOU OWE IT TO YOURSELF TO PURSUE YOUR DESTINY.

THANK YOU FATHER. I *NEEDED* TO HEAR THAT. I *WILL* DO WHAT I KNOW TO BE RIGHT.

OF COURSE, YOU MUST NOT HARM OTHERS IN YOUR-- MY SON, WHAT WAS THAT SOUND?

BLESS YOU FATHER, FOR YOU HAVE SINNED.

BLAM!

PETER DAVID
WRITER

RICH BUCKLER
PENCILER

BRETT BREEDING
JOSEF RUBINSTEIN
KYLE BAKER
PAT REDDING
INKERS

PHIL FELIX
LETTERER

GEORGE ROUSSOS
COLORIST

JIM OWSLEY
EDITOR

JIM SHOOTER
EDITOR IN CHIEF

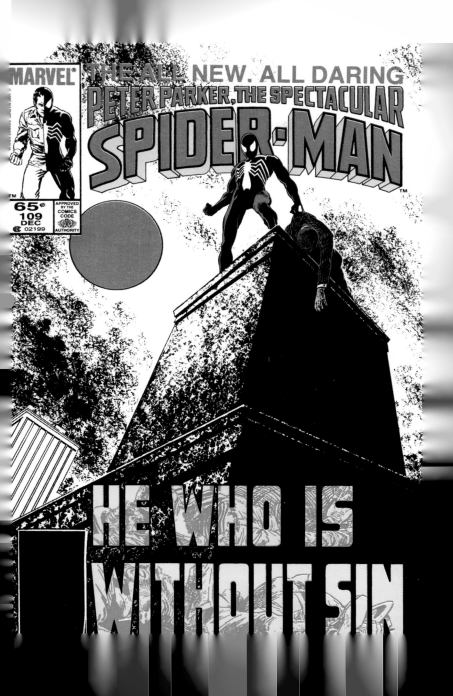

THE DEATH OF JEAN DeWOLFF PART 3

Stan Lee PRESENTS: **"HE WHO IS WITHOUT SIN"**

LOCAL RESIDENTS WERE *STUNNED* TONIGHT AT THE VIOLENT DEATH OF REVEREND BERNARD FINN, APPARENTLY AT THE HANDS OF THE MASKED MURDERER NAMED *SIN-EATER.*

THE REVEREND WAS KNOWN FOR HIS PUBLIC SPIRITEDNESS, AND HIS OUTSPOKENESS ON PRISON REFORM...

REV. BERNARD FINN

WHO WILL BE NEXT?

AUTHORITIES BELIEVE THAT IT WAS REVEREND FINN'S CONCERN FOR CRIMINALS--A CONCERN SHARED BY THE LATE JUDGE *HORACE ROSENTHAL*--

--THAT MARKED HIM AS A *TARGET* FOR THE SIN-EATER, WHO WAS SEEN *RUNNING* FROM THE CHURCH MOMENTS AFTER THE SHOOTING.

REVEREND FINN IS THE *FOURTH* KNOWN VICTIM OF THE SIN-EATER, WHO BEGAN A KILLING SPREE SEVERAL DAYS AGO.

HOURS AGO, *HUGO KELSEY*, A *BY-STANDER* DURING A BATTLE BETWEEN *SIN-EATER* AND *SPIDER-MAN*, DIED FROM GUNSHOT WOUNDS FROM A BLAST FROM SIN-EATER'S RIFLE.

A BLAST I *DODGED!* STAN, I--I COST THAT GUY HIS *LIFE!*

IT ALL HAPPENED SO *FAST*. I SHOULD HAVE WEBBED THE GUN, BUT I DODGED INSTINCTIVELY-- AND NOW SOME-ONE'S *DEAD!*

EVEN WHEN I USE MY POWERS FOR *GOOD*, INNOCENT PEOPLE GET HURT... KILLED, EVEN!

SPIDER-MAN, TAKE IT FROM A VETEREN *COP--NOBODY* MAKES ALL THE RIGHT DECISIONS ALL THE TIME.

BESIDES, SIN-EATER'S GUN-- THE ONE YOU BENT WHEN HE *HIT* YOU -- IT'S A *SCATTER* GUN. EVEN IF YOU'D *TAKEN* THE BULLETS, YOU'D BE DEAD AND KELSEY WOULD BE, TOO.

COMMUNITY LEADERS WERE OUTRAGED AND CALLED FOR...

OY VAY! NOW THEY'RE INTERVIEWING REVEREND *TOLLIVER*. *JUST* WHAT I NEED-- THAT GUY STIRRING THINGS UP EVEN *MORE*.

I HATE WORKING ON THIS CASE. I REALLY DO.

BETTY? IT'S MARLA JAMESON. LOOK, WITH BOTH JONAH AND NED AWAY AT THE DISTRIBUTOR CONFERENCE, HOW ABOUT IF WE TWO ABANDONED WIVES TEAM UP? STAY HERE AT THE HOUSE TOGETHER. THERE'S *PLENTY* OF ROOM...

YES. YES, I'M KIND OF NERVOUS *MYSELF* THESE DAYS, WHAT WITH THIS "SIN-EATER" MANIAC RUN-NING AMOK. I'M *JUMPING* AT EVERY NOISE. NO PLACE SEEMS *SAFE--!*

GREAT! I'LL SEE YOU THEN. AND, BETTY... *THANKS.*

2

I AM *STUNNED* THAT THE POLICE ARE UNABLE TO PROTECT EVEN A HOLY MAN IN THIS CITY. I JUST HOPE THAT, SINCE REVEREND FINN WAS *BLACK*, HE WILL NOT RECEIVE SHORT SHRIFT AT THE HANDS OF THE DETECTIVES.

WELL-SPOKEN, REV--IF I SAY SO *MYSELF*.

POLICE ARE REPORTEDLY WORKING ON *SEVERAL* LEADS TO THE SIN-EATER'S IDENTITY. THE MAIN CONCERN BY INSIDERS IS THAT THERE MAY BE *MORE* THAN *ONE* PERSON COMMITTING THE MURDERS...

...OR THAT THE CRIMES MAY PROMPT A RASH OF *COPYCAT* KILLINGS.

IN *OTHER* CRIME NEWS, ALLEGED DRUG DEALER *GERALD JABLONSKI*, HAD CHARGES DROPPED AGAINST HIM TODAY WHEN IT WAS DISCOVERED THAT EVIDENCE OBTAINED BY THE STATE ...

...WAS DONE SO *IMPROPERLY*, AND THAT EVIDENCE WAS RULED *INADMISSIBLE*. JABLONSKI IS QUOTED AS SAYING, "THANK HEAVENS, THE SYSTEM *WORKS*."

POLICE ARE *ALSO* PUZZLED BY A SERIES OF *BURGLARIES* ON THE *EAST SIDE* RECENTLY...

"POLICE ARE *UNSURE* OF HOW THE BURGLAR OR BURGLARES GAIN EN-TRANCE. ONLY *SMALL* OBJECTS OR *PORTABLE* ITEMS, SUCH AS SMALL TELEVISIONS, ARE BEING TAKEN, IMPLYING A SMALL *ONE-MAN* OPERATION."

TAP TAP

HMNH?

HUNH!?

SANTA!

WHISPER, HONEY.

SANTA, WHAT ARE YOU *DOING* HERE? CHRIST-MAS EVE ISN'T FOR--

LET ME *IN* AND I'LL TELL YOU.

OKAY. HOLD IT A SECOND...

THERE. UNLOCKED. SANTA, *THIS* YEAR I WAS GOING TO LEAVE YOU OUT OREOS INSTEAD OF CHOCOLATE CHIP COOKIES FOR A SNACK.

MY DADDY SAID YOU LIKE OREOS *BEST.* JUST LIKE HE DOES. IS THAT *TRUE?*

YES, I *LOVE* OREOS.

JUST LET ME SLIDE THIS WINDOW UP AND WE'LL *TALK.*

HO HO HO...

4

IT IS LATER THAT SAME NIGHT, AND *ANOTHER FAT MAN* -- WHO IS *HARDLY JOLLY* -- DICTATES INTO A SMALL RECORDER...

A LETTER TO MS. C.B. KALISH. DEAR MS. KALISH--

HOWEVER, YOUR RECENT ASSAULT ON TWO OF MY *MEN,* IN YOUR *GUISE* AS MADAME FATE WAS NEITHER *WELCOME* NOR *APPRECIATED.* NOR WAS IT *NECESSARY.*

I AM AWARE OF YOUR RECENT *ATTEMPTS* TO CONTACT ME WITH REGARDS TO BECOMING AS YOU PUT IT, MY NEW STAFF ASSASSIN.

I HAVE NO NEED FOR ASS-ASSINS, STAFF OR OTHER-WISE. MY BUSINESS DEALINGS ARE *QUITE* LEGAL. AT THIS TIME I SHALL TAKE *NO* ACTION AGAINST YOU SINCE I PERSONALLY--

--ABHOR VIOLENCE.

THIS IS YOUR ONLY WARNING. SINCERELY, WILSON FISK.

SPIDER-MAN, I AM *NOT* INTERESTED IN TRADING *QUIPS, BLOWS,* OR ANY OTHER *CHILDISH* INDULGENCES. YOU ARE *TRESPASSING,* AND IF YOU DO NOT LEAVE SHORTLY I SHALL CALL THE *POLICE.*

HAVEN'T GOT THE *NERVE* TO SIGN LETTERS WITH YOUR PSEUDONYM-- *KINGPIN?*

I ASSUME YOU CAME HERE FOR THE SAME REASON YOUR FRIEND *DAREDEVIL* DID SOME MINUTES AGO. YOU SEEK THIS *"SIN-EATER"* FELLOW. 5

I CANNOT HELP YOU IN THIS.

I SUGGEST YOU MIGHT CHECK WITH THE *LOWER* RUNGS OF GARBAGE THAT EXIST IN THE SHADOWY WORLD OF THE CRIMINAL -- PERHAPS *THEY* HAVE THE INFORMATION YOU WANT.

OH, I *WILL*, KINGPIN. YOU'RE JUST MY *FIRST* STOP. MAKE NO MISTAKE...

I'M GETTING THE MONSTER WHO KILLED JEAN DeWOLFF.

I DID NOT LIKE CAPTAIN DeWOLFF, NOR JUDGE ROSENTHAL. THEY WERE BOTH HONEST...

AND, HONEST PEOPLE BORE ME.

BUT SOMEONE WHO KILLS *PRIESTS* I HAVE NO TRUCK WITH. PRIEST KILLERS *POLARIZE* CITIES, AND SUCH CITIES ARE HARDER TO *CONTROL.*

YOU MAY LEAVE NOW, SPIDER-MAN. AND, BY THE WAY--

--I TRUST YOU WILL NOT FIND IT NECESSARY TO RENDER ANY MORE OF MY GUARDS UNCONSCIOUS ON YOUR WAY OUT.

6

YOU MIGHT LEARN A FEW POINTS OF *SUBTLETY* FROM YOUR FRIEND, DAREDEVIL.

HE MERELY KNOCKED ON THE FRONT DOOR.

ACROSS TOWN --

MY TALK WITH KINGPIN DIDN'T HELP ANY. MAYBE MY MISTAKE'S BEEN IN TRYING TO WORK THIS AS DAREDEVIL IN THE FIRST PLACE.

NOT THAT MATT MURDOCK, BLIND CRIMINAL ATTORNEY, COULD DO MUCH BETTER, BUT WITH MY HYPER SENSES AND BUILT-IN "RADAR SENSE"...

... I CAN EASILY INFILTRATE THIS DEN OF INIQUITY AS *JOE SHMOE,* FACELESS NOBODY. MAYBE "JOE" CAN SUCCEED WHERE D.D. FAILED.

AFTER ALL, THESE SLEAZEBALLS DON'T TAKE WELL TO MASKED ADVENTURERS LOOKING FOR LEADS.

CRASHING IN THROUGH THE WINDOW IN FULL COSTUME WOULD BE THE WORST POSSIBLE WAY TO HANDLE THIS.

EXCUSE ME, UHM, GENTLEMEN. I'M AFTER THE GUY WHO OFFED THE *PRIEST.*

IF ANY OF YOU CAN *HELP* ME, I'LL MAKE IT WORTH YOUR *WHILE.*

IF *NOT,* I'LL BE ON MY WAY.

YEAH? LET'S SEE YOUR *MONEY.*

LET'S SEE YOUR INFORMATION.

LET'S SEE YOUR *FACE* COME OFF!

7

ANYONE *ELSE* FEELING MORE COOPERATIVE?

CAN'T HELP YOU, SLICK.

AIN'T NONE OF US KNOW ABOUT THIS *SIN-EATER* GUY. BUT IF YOU *GET* THE SCUMBALL--

GIVE HIM ONE FOR *US!*

I WILL.

FOR *ONCE!* FOR *ONCE* NOBODY BROKE THE WIN--

NOBODY MOVE! I WANT INFORMATION ABOUT THE *SIN-EATER!*

KRASH!

AND IF I DON'T GET IT HERE, I'M GOING TO TEAR APART THIS TOWN UNTIL I *DO.*

AND IF WE *DON'T* WANT TO *GIVE YA* OUR HELP?

THEN I'LL *TAKE* IT!

GET *AWAY* FROM HIM! I *SAW* HIM LIKE THIS ONCE, WHEN HE WAS SEARCHING FOR THE *MASTER PLANNER.*

HE'LL KEEP GOING 'TILL HE *GETS* WHAT HE *WANTS!*

OH! WHO ARE *YOU?*

I'M HERE TO SEE ... UH...YOUR *DADDY.*

HE'S IN THE *BATHROOM.* HOLD ON. I'LL CALL HIM.

DAAADEEEE! THERE'S A MAN HERE WITH A *BUG* ON HIS CHEST!

A MAN WITH A WHAT ON HIS WH-- HOLY...

SUSIE, GET AWAY FROM HIM! *QUICK!*

WH-WHAT DO YOU *WANT?*

WHY, JUST TO HAVE A CHAT WITH YOU, *GERALD.* LET'S GO.

HEY, *C'MON.* NOT IN FRONT OF MY *KID.* C'MON, LEGGO!

WHERE ARE YOU GOING WITH MY *DADDY?!*

ON AN OUTING, HON'. WE'LL BE BACK BEFORE YOU *KNOW* IT!

GREAT. I CAN'T EVEN PUMP CRUMBS LIKE GERALD JABLONSKI WITHOUT FEELING LIKE ATTILA THE HUN.

DADDY! COME BACK! DAAA- DEEEE!

I HEARD ABOUT YOU ON THE *NEWS* THE OTHER DAY, GERRY. ABOUT HOW YOU BEAT THAT *DRUG RAP.*

SO I SAID TO MYSELF, *"SELF,"* I SAID, "GERRY DESERVES TO GO OUT AND *CELEBRATE* HIS WIN.

BUT, YOU'RE SUCH A HARD WORKER I KNEW YOU'D HAVE TO BE, WELL, *FORCED.*

HOW COULD YOU BRING ME *HERE?!* HALF THE HIRED THUGS IN THE CITY HANG OUT HERE!!

SURE! I'VE EVEN WALTZED MOST OF 'EM *AROUND* THE PAST FEW DAYS, SO THEY'LL LEAVE *ME* ALONE.

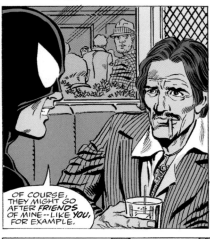

OF COURSE, THEY MIGHT GO AFTER *FRIENDS* OF MINE -- LIKE *YOU,* FOR EXAMPLE.

M-ME?

YOU GOT A BAD *STAMMER,* KNOW THAT, GERRY?

AND *YES,* I MEAN YOU! WE'RE PALS, AREN'T WE, GERRY? I MEAN, I'VE BEEN TO YOUR HOUSE, MET YOUR LOVELY SUSIE...

HECK, WE'RE PRACTICALLY *RELATED!*

FOR P-PITY'S SAKE, KEEP YOUR VOICE *DOWN!*

WELL, I'M GLAD WE HAD THIS CHAT. I'LL BE SEEING YOU AROUND, PAL!

12

WAIT A MINUTE! YOU CAN'T JUST *LEAVE!*

NO?

LOOK AT THESE GUYS! THEY THINK YOU'RE MY CHUM. IF YOU LEAVE ME NOW I'M *DEAD!*

OKAY! *OKAY!* I'M JUST THE MIDDLE MAN. GET ME IM-MUNITY AND I'LL FINGER THE BIG MEN FOR YOU --

I'M NOT THE *D.A.** BESIDES, I WANT THE SIN-EATER.

GEE. DEAD. LIKE THOSE KIDS YOU SIPHON DRUGS TO?

* DISTRICT ATTORNEY --OWZ.

WHAT, THE GUY WHO KILLED THE PRIEST AND COP AND JUDGE? I KNOW ZIP ABOUT HIM. I SWEAR.

NICE SEEING YOU, GERRY!

PLEASE! DON'T *LEAVE* ME!

I SWEAR I DON'T KNOW *ANY-THING* ABOUT THIS SIN-EATER!

ON MY DAUGHTER'S LIFE, I SWEAR.

ALL RIGHT. ALL RIGHT GERRY, I BELIEVE YOU.

LET'S GO CHAT WITH THE COPS.

DON'T LET THEM HURT ME...

I WON'T.

NEXT DAY...

KINGPIN SAID *DAREDEVIL* WAS LOOKING FOR SIN-EATER, TOO.

WONDER WHAT OLD HORN-HEAD'S INTEREST IN THIS IS?

GREAT. LANCE BANNON'S COZYING UP TO ROBBIE FOR PHOTO ASSIGN-MENTS. WONDER WHY *HE* DOESN'T GO THROUGH KATHRYN CUSHING?

YOU KNOW, BETTY, I'M ALMOST SORRY JONAH'S COMING BACK TOMORROW.

I KNOW, MARLA. US TWO "GIRLS" ON OUR OWN--

--I HAVEN'T HAD THIS MUCH FUN SINCE HIGH SCHOOL.

WHERE'S JAMESON?

EEEEEEEE

SLAM

IT'S HIM!

IT'S HIM?

IT'S HIM!

I WANT JONAH JAMESON!

BRING THAT POOR EXCUSE OF A *PUBLISHER* TO ME, NOW! OR--

--OR *SHE* DIES!

14

I'M JONAH JAMESON, SON. DON'T HURT HER.

WHY NOT PUT DOWN THE GUN? YOU NEED HELP, SON.

I'M NOT YOUR SON, SINNER!

ROBBIE, YOU BRAVE IDIOT! I CAN'T HOLD BACK--WAIT! THAT TYPEWRITER...

I'M GOING TO LIST YOUR CRIMES, SINNER--

LIST AWAY, NUTCASE. GIVE ME THREE SECONDS TO GET THIS ROLLER OUT OF THE TYPEWRITER--

--AND RIP OFF DARE-DEVIL'S STYLE.

ROBBIE! DUCK!

WHA--

WHAM!

UNGH!

WOW! THE POWER OF THE PRESS! PETE, THAT WAS--

LUCKY. JUST LUCKY. ROBBIE'S THE HERO.

HERO. RIGHT. NOW EXCUSE ME-- I THINK I'M GOING TO BE SICK.

15

HE WENT DOWN MUCH EASIER THAN WHEN I FOUGHT HIM BEFORE.

MAYBE IT'S 'CAUSE I CAUGHT HIM OFF GUARD. SURE, *THAT'S* IT.

I *GOT* HIM, JEAN ...

"I GOT HIM."

MR. GREGG, AS YOUR COUNSEL, I AM ADVISING YOU NOT TO SAY ANYTHING ...

IT WAS THE *VOICES*. I HAD TO DO IT.

COULDN'T RESIST VOICES IN THE NIGHT.

WHERE'S STAN? HE'S GOING TO HATE MISSING THIS.

MR. GREGG--

IT WAS THE VOICES ... THEY SAID WHEN AND WHERE.

I DIDN'T WANT TO AT FIRST. I DIDN'T THINK I *HAD*.

BUT THE PEOPLE DIED, SO IT *MUST* HAVE BEEN ME, RIGHT?

16

WHA--?
DAREDEVIL?!

AW, C'MON! BAD ENOUGH I'M LETTING SPIDER-MAN IN ON THIS. AT LEAST HE FOUGHT THIS GUY!

I ENCOUNTERED THE SUSPECT TOO, OFFICER. DON'T WORRY, I'LL STAY OUT OF YOUR WAY. WHERE IS HE?

SITTING RIGHT IN FRONT OF YOU! WHAT'RE YOU, BLIND?

I WANTED TO WARN THE PRIEST HE WOULD DIE.

I TRIED TWICE, BUT COULDN'T.

SO I TOOK ABSOLUTION FOR MY SINS. SO MANY SINS...

GENTLEMEN, I MUST PROTEST THIS--

MY HEART BLEEDS, PAL.

JAMESON WAS ACTUALLY SUPPOSED TO DIE TONIGHT AT HIS HOUSE. SO I FIGURED IF I GO EARLY EVERYTHING WILL BE WRONG AND I'LL BE CAUGHT.

AND IT WORKED. I HOPE THE VOICES AREN'T ANGRY...

SPIDER-MAN...

WE HAVE TO TALK. PRIVATELY. NOW.

CAN THIS WAIT, HORNHEAD? I --

NOW.

OKAY, OKAY...

YOU'VE GOT A COPY-CAT. HE'S NOT THE MAN WHO KILLED THE JUDGE. MAYBE HE DIDN'T KILL ANYONE.

YOU'RE KIDDING! HE WAS CAUGHT AT THE BUGLE...

HIS RIFLE'S THE SAME, EVEN WITH THE SAME BEND WHERE IT HIT ME. HE KNOWS DETAILS OF THE CRIMES. HIS MENTAL HEALTH RECORD IS--

I DON'T CARE. IT'S NOT HIM. TRUST ME.

HOW CAN I EXPLAIN TO SPIDER-MAN MY ABILITY TO DISTINGUISH PEOPLE BY THEIR HEARTBEATS...?

17

"ALL RIGHT, *DD*. LET'S SAY I TOSS LOGIC. IF HE'S NOT SIN-EATER, WHO IS?"

"I DON'T KNOW. DID YOU CATCH HIS ADDRESS?"

"LET ME THINK. YEAH. ON BLEEKER, IN THE VILLAGE."

WHAT A MESS! ARE YOU CONVINCED, HORN-HEAD?

SLOVENLINESS IS HARDLY A CRIMINAL OFFENSE.

BY THE WAY, I HEAR THAT GERALD JABLONSKI IS TURNING STATE'S EVIDENCE. HE'LL BE GIVEN PROTEC-TION. THE WORKS. WORD HAS IT YOU'RE RE-SPONSIBLE.

YOU CAN THANK ME LATER.

OH REALLY? AREN'T YOU BOTHERED THAT YOUR ACTIONS ENDANGERED JABLONSKI'S LIFE?

THAT HE WAS FORCED TO TESTIFY BECAUSE HE FELT HE'D BEEN PUT IN AN UNTEN-ABLE POSI-TION.

JABLONSKI IS A DRUG-PUSHING CREEP. I THOUGHT HE MIGHT LEAD ME TO SIN-EATER, AND IT WAS THE ONLY WAY I COULD THINK OF TO PRESSURE HIM.

AND DON'T GO HOLIER-THAN-THOU ON ME, HORNHEAD. YOU'VE NEVER ROUGHED ANYONE UP FOR YOUR OWN NEEDS?

THIS WASN'T ROUGHING UP! THIS WAS COERCION.

THIS WAS PUTTING A MAN IN FEAR OF HIS LIFE FOR YOUR OWN REASONS. AND I DON'T CARE HOW NOBLE YOUR MOTIVES WERE.

IT STILL STINKS.

18

THIS DOOR IS LOCKED OFF. MUST BE TO THE NEXT APARTMENT. BUT--

--IT APPEARS TO HAVE BEEN JIMMIED RECENTLY.

THIS CON ED BILL...HOLY COW! THIS IS STAN CARTER'S PLACE! STAN'S GONNA FREAK WHEN HE FINDS OUT HE'S BEEN LIVING NEXT DOOR TO THE--

Con Edison

SPIDER-MAN...

NO... OH, NO...

SIN-EATER'S GEAR...IN STAN'S CLOSET BUT THAT'S IMPOS...

THERE'S A RECORDER OVER THERE. MY GUESS IS THAT THIS CARTER RECORDED SOME SORT OF DIARY AT NIGHT...

GREGG'S BED IS ON THE OTHER SIDE OF THE WALL.

GREGG, ALREADY IN A STRAINED MENTAL STATE, HEARD THE VOICES THROUGH THE WALL AND CONVINCED HIMSELF HE WAS THE SIN-EATER.

NO. IT CAN'T BE. IF YOU CAN'T TELL THE VICTIMS FROM THE KILLERS ANYMORE, THEN THERE'S NOTHING ...

LISTEN, BLAST IT! THERE'S TWO EMPTY GUN HOLDERS. GREGG MUST HAVE BUSTED IN AND TAKEN ONE--

--BUT THERE'S ONE UNACCOUNTED FOR.

AND THE NEXT VICTIM IS SUPPOSED TO BE...

19

JAMESON... BUT JAMESON IS IN FLORIDA... WITH NED LEEDS...

AND BETTY LEEDS IS... STAYING WITH... MARLA...

OH NO.

THE BUGLE. SHE MUST STILL BE AT THE BUGLE.

SHE USUALLY WORKS LATE.

PLEASE LET HER BE THERE.

ROBBIE. IS BETTY LEEDS THERE?

SHE WHAT?

YOU'LL BE GLAD YOU LEFT EARLY, BETTY. I'VE BEEN TAKING COOKING LESSONS. YOU'LL LOVE WHAT'S COMING.

I'LL BE THERE IN A MINUTE TO HELP, MARLA. I'M JUST FINISHING A LETTER TO MY MOM.

SHE WORRIES ABOUT ME.

CALM DOWN, SPIDER-MAN. IT'S 555-2786.

JONAH WOULD KILL ME IF HE KNEW I GAVE YOU HIS HOME NUMBER. WILL YOU PLEASE--

HELLO?

BETTY AND MARLA MUST BE BACK AT JAMESON'S BY NOW. AND CARTER MAY BE WAITING FOR THEM.

HE IS! I KNOW IT!

IF THAT MONSTER HURTS THEM...HURTS ANYONE...

I'LL KILL HIM.

20

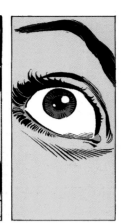

"HE WHO IS WITHOUT SIN"

PETER DAVID
Writer

RICH BUCKLER
Pencil Art

BRETT BREEDING
Finished Art

PHIL FELIX
Lettering

NEL YOMTOV
Coloring

JIM OWSLEY
Editor

JIM SHOOTER
Editor In Chief

WHEN I FIRST MET BETTY BRANT, I WAS A SHY, BESPECTACLED BOOKWORM.

NO GIRL HAD EVER GLANCED AT ME BEFORE, AND THEN BETTY...

BETTY JUMP-STARTED MY HEART.

BUT THE SHADOW OF *SPIDER-MAN* CAME BETWEEN US, DROVE HER INTO THE ARMS OF NED LEEDS.

WE FINALLY RECONCILED TO A CAUTIOUS FRIENDSHIP-- BUT SHE ALWAYS SENSED I HID SOME PART OF MY LIFE FROM HER.

WELL, NOW I'M COMING *OUT* OF THE SHADOWS, TO AVENGE HER DEATH AT THE HANDS OF THE *SIN-EATER*.

AND HEAVEN *HELP* HIM, BECAUSE NOTHING'S GOING TO SAVE HIM NOW.

THE DEATH OF JEAN DEWOLFF

conclusion

ALL MY SINS REMEMBERED

FIRST TIME I'VE EVER MISSED.

YET THE LORD'S HAND MUST HAVE *GUIDED* YOU TO SEEK COVER UNDER THE DESK, FOR I DO *HIS* WORK.

RISE, MY CHILD. YOU ARE OBVIOUSLY *NOT* THE SINNER, J. JONAH JAMESON.

MUH... MUH....

WHERE IS JAMESON, EH?

MUH... MARLA...?

YOUR FRIEND IS GONE. I HEARD THE FRONT DOOR SLAM...

DO YOU WORK FOR THE SINNER JAMESON?

YES, UH, NO.

A SHAME YOU CHOSE TO *ALLY* YOURSELF WITH THAT CURSED NEWSPAPER PUBLISHER.

IF I CAN'T HAVE *JAMESON*, I'LL LEAVE A MESSAGE WITH *YOU*--

YOU CAN DELIVER IT--

WHEN YOU SEE HIM IN THE *AFTERLIFE*.

YOU? YOU'RE NOTHING. I WANTED *JAMESON* BECAUSE HE OPPOSES MASKED VIGILANTES.

I KILLED THE PRIEST BECAUSE HE OPPOSED CAPITAL PUNISHMENT...

I KILLED THE *JUDGE* BECAUSE HE CODDLED CRIMINALS...

WHU... WHY? WHY... MUH...ME...?

AND I KILLED JEAN DEWOLFF...

...BECAUSE I FELT LIKE IT.

CHUT

ARRRGHH!

YOU... SLUT!

STAB *ME* WITH A LETTER OPENER, WILL YOU? I'LL--

≷GASP!≷ IT'S... IT'S...

WHAT ARE YOU BABBLING A--

YOU *WANT* THE HARLOT, SPIDER-MAN? TAKE HER! YOU *DESERVE* EACH OTHER.

BETTY! ALIVE!

OBVIOUSLY.

GIVE ME A MOMENT AND I'LL REMEDY THAT.

NO.' I DON'T KNOW HOW, BUT I'VE BEEN GIVEN A *SECOND* CHANCE.

AND I'M *NOT* GONNA BLOW IT.

FIRST WE RELIEVE YOU OF YOUR TCY.

TOY?! YOU CRETIN! THAT'S THE VOICE OF GOD! IT'S PART OF *ME*!

PART OF YOU, HUH? *WHICH* PART?

HOW ABOUT YOUR *NECK*?

KRACK

YOU WERE LAUGHING AT ME ALL ALONG, RIGHT, CARTER?

ACTED LIKE A FRIEND WHEN IT WAS ALL A SICK JOKE.

YOU DISGUSTING--

IT'S THE QUIET, UNOBVIOUS NUTS THAT YOU HAVE TO WATCH.

I'M... ...I'M SORRY.

SORRY?!

DON'T GIVE ME SORRY!

WHUMF!

TELL IT TO THE JUDGE!

--OR TO THE PRIEST!

--OR BETTER YET--

--TELL IT TO JEAN DeWOLFF!

WHAMM!

SPIDER-MAN'S HEART IS POUNDING LIKE A TRIPHAMMER. I'VE NEVER KNOWN HIM TO BE THIS... *BRUTAL!*

SPIDER-MAN! BACK OFF, IT'S OVER.

IT'S *NOT!* HE MIGHT STILL GET LOOSE, KILL SOMEONE. IT WON'T BE OVER UNTIL--

UNTIL HE'S *DEAD?*

GET A GRIP ON YOURSELF, MAN! HE'S NO LONGER A THREAT!

THE ONLY THREAT HERE IS *YOU!!*

OUT OF MY WAY!

IF YOU WANT HIM--

--YOU'LL HAVE TO COME THROUGH *ME.*

THWAM!

I *WARNED* YOU KEEP *OUT* OF THIS.

THIS IS BETWEEN *CARTER* AND *ME!*

[83]

DON'T YOU DARE MAKE ME SOUND LIKE SIN-EATER!

YOU TALK AS IF I ATTACK INNOCENT PEOPLE, LIKE HE DOES!

HE'S FURIOUS, SWINGING WILD. GOOD. I CAN USE THAT.

I USE MY POWERS TO PROTECT PEOPLE *FROM* CRIMINALS!

AND WHAT MAKES A CRIMINAL?

A CROOK'S A CROOK! WHAT'RE YOU, NUTS?

YOU'RE RIGHT! WE HAVE TO STOP CROOKS.

CROOKS LIKE YOU!

WHAT?

COME ON, SPIDER-MAN, I READ THE PAPERS. I KNOW ALL ABOUT YOU!

AND I'M TAKING YOU DOWN-- *CRIMINAL!*

THWAK!

YOU'RE *TWISTING* EVERYTHING! YOU SHOULD BE A LAWYER.

AND DON'T THINK YOU CAN CATCH ME FROM *BEHIND* WITH THAT BILLY-CLUB OF YOURS!

MY SPIDER-SENSE CAN TRACK ANYTHING. WAIT, IT'S STILL--

ANYTHING. BUT NOT EVERYTHING. NOT IN *YOUR* MENTAL STATE.

B'NAM!

URMFF!

I'VE BEEN LUCKY. I MANAGED TO DISTRACT HIS SPIDER-SENSE WITH HALF MY CLUB--

AND NAIL HIM WITH THE OTHER HALF. BUT I CAN'T LET UP.

WHAM!

IF I GIVE HIM THE SLIGHTEST CHANCE, HE'LL WIPE THE FLOOR WITH ME.

FINALLY...

INCREDIBLE. A DOZEN PUNCHES AND HE'S BARELY OUT.

HIS HEARTBEAT'S STILL STRONG. ONLY A FEW MINUTES BEFORE HE COMES TO.

SECONDS LATER...

THE ONLY REASON I BEAT HIM WAS BECAUSE HE WAS SO EMOTIONALLY WORKED UP.

BUT SIN-EATER KILLED A CLOSE FRIEND OF MINE-- AND I'VE STILL GOT MY "PROFESSIONAL DETACHMENT."

SO DOES SPIDER-MAN FEEL TOO MUCH? OR DO I FEEL...TOO *LITTLE*?

MRS. LEEDS, HOW DO YOU FEEL BEING ALIVE?

GO AWAY.

WHEN I HEARD THE BLAST, I TRIED TO CALL THE POLICE, BUT THE PHONE WAS OFF THE HOOK.

SO I RAN OUTSIDE, CALLED THE POLICE... OH, BETTY... I SHOULD HAVE--

WHAT? RISKED YOUR LIFE? MARLA, YOU DID THE RIGHT THING. JUST BE GLAD WE'RE BOTH ALIVE.

YOU'RE REMARKABLE. SO CALM. SO--

ONCE AGAIN, THE SUSPECTED "SIN-EATER" HAS BEEN APPREHENDED--

-- AFTER THREATENING THE PERSONAL SECRETARY OF PUB--

THREATENED?! HE TRIED TO *KILL* ME!!

THE SUSPECT HAS BEEN IDENTIFIED AS DETECTIVE STAN CARTER OF THE 14TH PRECINCT.

IT IS NOW BELIEVED THAT AN EARLIER APPREHENDED SUSPECT IS NOT--

A COP--? DID HE SAY--?

A COP! A LOUSY, STINKIN' COP.

"IRONICALLY, CARTER HIMSELF WAS ASSIGNED AS THE DETECTIVE IN CHARGE OF THE MURDER INVESTIGATION OF CAPTAIN JEAN DeWOLFF, FIRST KNOWN VICTIM OF THE SIN-EATER."

OH, GEEZ, STAN... WHY?

GET LIEUTENANT... SORRY, *CAPTAIN* D'ANGELO... ON THE PHONE.

HE'S INHERITED JEAN'S COMMAND...

WHY SHOULD HE GET ANY EXTRA SLEEP?

THIS IS JUST WONDERFUL. I CAN IMAGINE WHAT THE PUBLIC IS SAYING.

FIRST YOU'RE NOT SAFE FROM THE CRIMINALS; NOW YOU'RE NOT SAFE FROM THE COPS!

I BET THEY REALLY KNEW AND THEY WERE COVERING FOR HIM. THEY STICK *TO-GETHER*, Y'KNOW.

UH-HUH. UH-HUH. WHAT ABOUT WHEN A BUNCH OF THEM SHOT THAT WOMAN? AND THEY GOT OFF?

I TELL YA, YA JUST CAN'T TRUST *ANYBODY!*

TIMMY?

TIMMY, I THOUGHT I HEARD YOU RATTLING AROUND? AWAY FROM THE *WINDOW*, SPORT, IT'S THE MIDDLE OF THE NIGHT.

BACK TO BED... SAY, WHAT ARE YOU *GRIN-NING* ABOUT?

IT'S A SECRET.

BUT YOU'RE GONNA GET SOMETHING *REALLY* GOOD FOR CHRISTMAS.

WELL, THAT'S NICE, TIMMY. GOOD NIGHT.

JUST WAIT UNTIL DAD FINDS OUT HE'S GETTING A GREAT BIG COLOR *TV* FROM SANTA. AND ALL I HAD TO DO--

HONEY, WHERE'S THE PORTABLE *TV?*

-- IS TRADE SANTA OUR LITTLE ONE.

...ho ho ho...

NEXT MORNING, IN THE LOBBY OF THE DAILY BUGLE...

UNDER-PRIVILEGED

BOY, THE "TOYS FOR THE UNDERPRIVILEGED" DRIVE IS SURE GETTING A PATHETIC TURNOUT THIS YEAR.

GUESS THE CITY ISN'T IN MUCH OF A GIVING MOOD RECENTLY.

THE OVERWHELMING FEELING SEEMS TO BE ANGER.

OUT OF MY WAY OR YOU'RE FIRED.

BUT I DON'T WORK HERE.

FINE, YOU'RE HIRED.

NOW YOU'RE THROUGH. GET *OUT.*

AND SPEAKING OF ANGRY MOODS... *HI, JONAH!*

HOW DID THE DISTRIBUTOR CONFERENCE GO?

FINE IF YOU ENJOY DEBACLES.

SOME WHOLESALER HATED MY CIGAR, SO NOW "NOW" MAGAZINE WON'T BE CARRIED IN CLEVELAND.

THEN OUR PLANE WAS DELAYED FOUR HOURS OUT OF FLORIDA, THEN WE WERE STACKED UP OVER... OH, *FORGET* IT.

HAVEN'T SEEN A PAPER YET. WHAT'S BEEN GOING ON, PARKER?

OH... WELL...

SIN-EATER BROKE INTO THE BUGLE CITY ROOM SHOUTING HE WANTED TO KILL YOU.

ROBBIE PRETENDED HE WAS YOU, CONFUSED SIN-EATER, AND WE DISARMED HIM.

TURNED OUT IT WASN'T *REALLY* HIM, THOUGH. ONLY A COPYCAT. SO THE *REAL* KILLER WENT TO YOUR HOUSE, JONAH, AND FOUND YOUR WIFE, MARLA. AND NED, BETTY WAS THERE, TOO.

BUT DON'T WORRY. SPIDER-MAN ARRIVED JUST IN TIME AND SAVED THEM. BEAT SIN-EATER TO A *PULP* HE'S IN POLICE CUSTODY NOW.

GUESS YOU BOTH OWE SPIDEY A DEBT YOU CAN *NEVER* REPAY.

NOT... SPIDER-MAN...

BUT... BUT... BUT...

HMMM. WONDER HOW *LONG* IT'LL BE BEFORE JONAH AND NED REALIZE THIS WAS THEIR FLOOR.

MESSAGE FOR YOU, PETER. OR SHOULD I CALL YOU "FLASH"...?

THANKS, ANNE. BUT LOOK, JUST 'CAUSE I'M A PHOTO-GRAPHER, IT DOESN'T MEAN YOU NICKNAME ME "FLASH." IN FACT, I'D PREFER YOU *DIDN'T.*

FINE, PETER. WORK AT *31* FLAVORS AND I'LL CALL YOU *"SCOOP."*

EVERYONE'S A COMEDIAN.

HI, AUNT MAY. YOU CALLED?

PETER, I HATE TO BOTHER YOU, BUT... IT'S ERNIE. HE WAS VERY UPSET THIS MORNING. ESPECIALLY AFTER HEARING THE NEWS ABOUT THAT AWFUL MAN.

DON'T *WORRY*, AUNT MAY. HE'S PROBABLY JUST BLOWING OFF STEAM. EVER SINCE THE MUGGING...

THAT'S WHAT *SCARES* ME, PETER. HE TOOK HIS OLD ARMY REVOLVER, HIS WAR MEMENTO.

OH, BOY. LOOK. I'LL KEEP A LOOKOUT FOR HIM. BUT MAYBE YOU SHOULD CALL THE *POLICE*.

OH, NO, PETER. I WOULDN'T WANT TO GET HIM IN TROUBLE.

BUT EVERYONE HERE AT THE HOUSE IS *VERY* CONCERNED.

I'LL GET RIGHT ON IT, AUNT MAY. BYE-BYE.

ALTHOUGH AUNT MAY DIDN'T SAY ANYTHING ABOUT IT, HER BOYFRIEND NATHAN WOUND UP IN THE HOSPITAL.* BECAUSE I DIDN'T KEEP CLOSE TABS ON HIM.* NOW'S MY CHANCE TO MAKE UP FOR IT.

*AMAZING SPIDEY #271 --OWZ.

PETER! GOOD. I NEED YOU TO GO WITH THE MAN-IN-THE-STREET REPORTER, SNYDER. TAKE HEAD SHOTS. NICE EASY STUFF.

BUT, ROBBIE, I HAVE TO LOOK FOR SOMEONE.

WELL, *NOW* YOU CAN LOOK FOR HIM AND MAKE *MONEY* AT THE SAME TIME.

BUT ROBBIE...

ALL RIGHT, SON. I'LL JUST TELL YOUR NEW BOSS, KATHRYN CUSHING, THAT YOU TURNED DOWN AN EASY ASSIGNMENT. YOU CAN GIVE YOUR REASONS TO HER.

UNLESS YOU'D *RATHER*...

HI. I'M IVAN SNYDER FROM *THE BUGLE*, ASKING TODAY'S MAN-IN-THE-STREET QUESTION...

CONSIDERING THE ALLEGED IDENTITY OF THE SIN-EATER, DO YOU FIND THE POLICE LESS *TRUSTWORTHY*?

YOU KIDDIN'? I *NEVER* TRUSTED THEM IN THE *FIRST* PLACE.

YOU *SHOULD* BE ABLE TO TRUST SOMEONE. BUT IT SEEMS YOU CAN'T TRUST *ANYONE*.

AND IF YOU TRUST THE WRONG PERSON... HEAVEN HELP YOU.

TERRIBLE WHAT YOU READ THESE DAYS.

ALL THOSE POOR PEOPLE THAT CRAZY MAN KILLED. DEFENSELESS.

CRIMINALS PICK ON THE DEFENSELESS ONES. ON PEOPLE LIKE ME... OR ME THE WAY I *ONCE* WAS.

IF IT WERE JUST THIS, BUT... YOU SEE EVERY DAY ABOUT THE POLICE HURTING PEOPLE. I THINK MAYBE THEY CRACK UNDER PRESSURE.

NO MORE, THOUGH. I WON'T COWER ANYMORE. NOW ERNIE POPCHIK FIGHTS FOR WHAT IS HIS.

THE WORLD TRADE CENTER IS NEXT. IT'LL BE NICE, LOOKING DOWN ON THE CITY AND FEELING LIKE I OWN IT-- BECAUSE I'M NOT AFRAID ANYMORE.

SAY NOW... THERE'S A FELLOW WHO MIGHT TAKE PITY ON OUR MISSING FRIEND. LET'S FIND OUT IF HE HAS ANY MONEY TO HELP US OUT.

YEAH... IN FACT, IT MAKES ME MAD. AND I'M NOT THE ONLY ONE. IN FACT, WE'RE GONNA...

UH... NO COMMENT. ON SECOND THOUGHT, NO COMMENT.

PARDON ME, GOOD SIR. WE HAVE A SICK FRIEND, AND WE NEED TO BUY HIM MEDICINE.

A MAN OF YOUR YEARS WOULD UNDERSTAND THE IMPORTANCE OF THIS.

B... THE MEDICINE'S VERY EXPENSIVE. WE NEED MONEY-- AS MUCH AS YOU HAVE ON YOU, PREFERABLY.

HOLY...

I ONLY HAVE ONE THING ON ME...

BUT I'M MORE THAN HAPPY TO *SHARE* IT WITH YOU.

BLAM

BLAM

BLAM

WORLD TRADE CENTER. WORLD TRADE CENTER, LAST STOP.

LAST STOP.

NO MORE PASSENGERS, PLEASE. THIS TRAIN IS NOW OUT OF SERVICE.

ALL PASSENGERS SHOULD NOW LEAVE THE TRAIN.

A SPECIAL BULLETIN. *WNBC* HAS JUST LEARNED EXCLUSIVELY THAT POLICE SERGEANT *STAN CARTER,* THE SIN-EATER SUSPECT, WILL BE *MOVED* THIS AFTERNOON TO RIKER'S ISLAND.

THE 14TH PRECINCT, WHERE CARTER IS CURRENTLY HELD, IS DEEMED UNSAFE DUE TO THE RARIFIED NATURE OF--

GREAT. JUST GREAT. D'ANGELO'LL HAVE KITTENS WHEN HE HEARS THIS LEAKED.

AND THAT MOB OUTSIDE LOOKS READY TO *LYNCH* STAN--OR WHERE *IS* D'ANGELO, ANYWAY?

IN HIS OFFICE, WITH *DA TOWER,* THE COMMANDER, AND BELIEVE IT OR NOT...

"AN AGENT OF SHIELD."

LET ME GET THIS STRAIGHT, JAMES BOND-- YOU'RE SAYING CARTER COULD GO FREE?

NO. BUT I'M SAYING THAT CARTER MAY NOT HAVE BEEN IN HIS RIGHT MIND.

GREAT. CARE TO EXPLAIN THAT?

CERTAINLY, MR. DISTRICT ATTORNEY. DURING HIS TIME AT SHIELD, STAN WAS IN R&D.

RESEARCH AND DEVELOPMENT? OF WHAT?

THE EXTRAORDINARY STRENGTH GAINED FROM SUCH DRUGS SUCH AS PCP OR ANGEL DUST. USERS REPORTEDLY BECOME UNSTOPPABLE JUGGERNAUTS IN SOME INSTANCES.

STAN AND SEVERAL OTHERS WERE INJECTED WITH MODIFICATIONS OF PCP TO SEE IF IT COULD BE USED SAFELY.

GOOD GRIEF. THAT'S FRIGHTENING.

R&D EVENTUALLY AGREED WITH YOU. THE TEST-DRUG IMPROVED STRENGTH, AND ENDURANCE, BUT WAS JUDGED TOO UNSTABLE. SIDE-EFFECTS SEEMED TOO NUMEROUS AND UNPREDICTABLE.

STAN DIDN'T TAKE THE DISCONTINUANCE OF THE PROGRAM VERY WELL.

STAN COMPLAINED THOSE IN AUTHORITY ACTED CAPRICIOUSLY, TOYED WITH PEOPLE'S LIVES. HE BECAME...WELL... VIOLENT.

WE THOUGHT, WHEN STAN LEFT THAT THERE WAS NO TRACE OF THE DRUGS IN HIS SYSTEM...

BUT IT'S POSSIBLE WE WERE WRONG, AND THAT THE RECENT DEATH OF HIS PARTNER...

UNHINGED HIM. WONDER-FUL.

JUST *WONDERFUL.* I'VE GOT A POLITICAL AND *PR* HOT POTATO...

AND NOW YOU'RE SAYING BECAUSE *YOUR* SCIENTISTS SCREWED UP...

I MAY HAVE TO ACCEPT AN *INSANITY* PLEA. THE PUBLIC'S GOING TO *CRUCIFY* US!

THIS LUNATIC KILLS BLACK PRIESTS, FOR PITY'S SAKE. BUT IT'S POSSIBLE THAT THE DOCTORS COULD CERTIFY HIM "OKAY" AFTER A YEAR OF MEDICAL OBSERVATION...

AND HE COULD WALK WITH NO JAIL TIME. IS THAT WHAT YOU'RE TELLING ME?

YES, I AM.

SWELL. NOW TELL *THEM!*

KRASH

COMING 'ROUND NOW, SIR.

WHERE THE BLAZES IS THAT RIKER'S TRUCK?! THEY'RE THROWING *BRICKS!*

BRING 'EM ROUND BACK. BREAK OUT SHIELDS AND RIOT CLUBS GENTLEMEN...

WE'RE UNDER SIEGE!

POLICE

IT'S GOOD ROBBIE PULLED ME OFF THAT MAN-IN-THE-STREET STUFF. THIS IS WHERE THE ACTION IS.

I WONDER HOW THEY'D FEEL IF THEY WERE ME... SUCKERED BY CARTER ALL ALONG THE WAY.

FOR INSTANCE, IF I'D BEEN THINKING, I'D HAVE REALIZED HE FAKED THAT CALL FROM BALLISTICS...

...SINCE YOU CAN'T MATCH AMMO FIRED FROM THAT TYPE OF GUN!

AND HIS CRACKS ABOUT BEING A SUSPECT, AND "UNOBVIOUS NUTS."

IT BURNS ME TO THINK HE WAS YANKING MY--UH-OH, SPIDEY SENSE WARNING ME...

DAREDEVIL! BETTER HIDE MY CAMERA!

YOU'VE GOT GUTS, COMING HERE. WHAT DID YOU MEAN WHEN YOU CALLED ME A CRIMINAL? AND MAKE IT GOOD OR I'LL CLEAN YOUR CLOCK FOR YOU!

MOST EVERYONE BELIEVES YOU'RE A CROOK, RIGHT, SPIDEY? BUT IF YOU WERE ARRESTED, WOULDN'T YOU DESERVE YOUR DAY IN COURT?

OR SHOULD YOU HAVE BEEN JUST TURNED OVER TO MOB JUSTICE? THE SAME TYPE OF MOB THAT WANTS STAN CARTER NOW.

I'M NOT STAN CARTER. BIG DIFFERENCE.

NOT IN MY EYES!

UH-OH. SPEAKING OF EYES, CAST YOURS DOWN THERE.

POL

JUS-TICE! JUS-TICE! JUS-TICE!

YOU'RE ALL IN IT TOGETHER! YOU'RE PRO-TECTING THAT SICKO! BRING HIM OUT!

BRING HIM OUT! BRING HIM OUT!

BRING HIM OUT! HURRY UP! WHILE THE CROWD'S DISTRACTED AROUND FRONT.

GOOD THING HE'S HEAVILY SEDATED. I WOULDN'T WANT TO TANGLE WITH SOMEONE WHO COULD GO THREE ROUNDS WITH SPIDER-MAN.

THAT'S HIM!

THAT'S THE CRUMB WHO KILLED MY DAUGHTER!

GET HIM! GET HIM FOR JEAN!

THEY'RE GOING TO KILL HIM!

SO?

CLEAR OUT, YOU PEOPLE! NOW!!

ANOTHER COSTUMED NUT! HE MUST BE THE COP'S PAL!

GET HIM!

SO MANY PEOPLE. RADAR SENSE IS COMPLETELY BOGGLED. I'M... I'M BLIND.

I'M CLOSING MY EYES. I WON'T WATCH.

BUT IS IT BECAUSE I'M AFRAID I'LL GO DOWN AND RESCUE CARTER--OR BECAUSE I'LL ENJOY SEEING HIM GET HIS JUST REWARDS.

LET DAREDEVIL SAVE HIM, HE'S SO WILD ABOUT CARTER I WASH MY HANDS OF IT.

SPIDER-MAN!!

NO GOOD! HE DOESN'T SEE OR HEAR ME... OR DOES NOT WANT TO. BUT I NEED HIS HELP, DESPERATELY.

UNCLE BEN... GWENDY... CAPTAIN STACY... NOW JEAN... I'VE LOST SO MANY LOVED ONES TO CRIMINALS.

I USE MY POWER TO PROTECT INNOCENTS. NOT... ANIMALS LIKE SIN-EATER.

IF I DID, THEN I WOULDN'T BE WORTHY OF THE NAME--

SPIDER-MAN!!

PETER!!

A NAME, CALLED OUT AS A LAST RESORT. A NAME THAT IS UNHEEDED BY ALL...

ALL SAVE THE MAN TO WHOM IT WAS ADDRESSED...

PETER PARKER, THE SPECTACULAR--

SPIDER-MUNNNGGHH!

ONE SIDE! I HAVE TO SAVE MY IDIOT FRIEND, HERE.

SIN-EATER. HAVE TO GET HIM.

I SEE HIM. BUT JEAN'S STEP-DAD SAW HIM FIRST.

YOU SLIME! YOU'LL NEVER ROB ANYONE OF THEIR CHILD AGAIN!

Y'HEAR, GARBAGE? NEVER AGAIN!

IF I HAD ANY CHOICE, FELLA, I'D HELP YOU.

BUT MY CHUM WON'T LEAVE WITHOUT THE MAN WHO'S WEARING YOUR FINGERPRINTS ON HIS THROAT.

BESIDES, MUCH AS IT HURTS...

I'M SUPPOSED TO BE ONE OF THE GOOD GUYS.

MINUTES LATER, THE CROWD HAS BEEN DISPERSED AND STAN CARTER SAFELY LOADED ONTO A TRUCK...

SPIDER-MAN, I'M SORRY I SHOUTED OUT LIKE THAT. I HAD TO DO SOMETHING TO MAKE YOU REALIZE HOW BAD THE SITUATION WAS.

NO HARM DONE, DD ALTHOUGH I NEVER EXPECTED THE MAN WITHOUT FEAR TO PANIC.

NO FEAR. THAT'S ME. BUT DESPERATION -- THAT I HAVE LOADS OF.

SO... "PETER," HUH?

YUP. AND IN CASE YOU'RE WONDERING, MY HANDLE IS...

...MATT MURDOCK.

YOU'RE KIDDING, RIGHT? I MEAN... MURDOCK'S BLIND...

... I MEAN...

...THAT IS...

... UH, LET'S GO SOMEPLACE AND TALK ABOUT THIS...

SOMETIME LATER--

FAINTLY ACRID, BUT A NICE APARTMENT.

BOY, YOU REALLY *MUST* BE BLIND. AND YEAH, I HAD A FIRE RECENTLY.

LET ME UNDERSTAND-- YOU COULD TELL WHEN YOU HEARD MY HEART-BEAT AS PETER PARKER AND LATER AS SPIDER-MAN THAT WE WERE THE SAME GUY? THAT'S SOME POWER. WHAT DO YOU CALL IT?

LISTENING.

THANKS AGAIN FOR SAVING MY HASH BACK THERE.

YOU STUCK UP FOR WHAT YOU BELIEVED. I COULDN'T LET THEM *KILL* YOU. YOU JUST BECAUSE YOU WERE DOING WHAT YOU FELT WAS *RIGHT*.

THEY FELT WHAT *THEY* WERE DOING WAS RIGHT. ARE YOU SAYING I WAS *MORE* RIGHT THAN THEY

I HESITATED. IF YOU HADN'T BEEN DOWN THERE, I DON'T KNOW IF I WOULD HAVE SAVED STAN. YOU... YOU WERE AN INNOCENT. STAN WASN'T.

UNDER THE LAW HE WAS. WE HAVE TO HAVE OUR *SYSTEM*, PETER, OR IT FALLS APART. AND, IF IT DOESN'T WORK, WE *MAKE* IT WORK. WE DON'T JUST IGNORE IT.
AGAIN, PETER, WHAT IF IT WERE *SPIDER-MAN*, ACCUSED CRIM-INAL, WITH HIS HEAD ON THE BLOCK. OR--

RRRING

HOLD ON, MATT, HELLO?

WH--AUNT MAY! HOLD IT. SLOW DOWN. WHAT--?

ERNIE POPCHIK'S UNDER *ARREST*? WHY?

HE SHOT *WHO*?

THREE TEENAGERS, PETER. THE WOUNDS AREN'T SERIOUS, BUT THE BOYS ARE IN THE *HOSPITAL*.

ERNIE TURNED HIMSELF IN-- SAID IT WAS *SELF-DEFENSE*, BUT THE BOYS WEREN'T *ARMED*. OH, PETER--

HE'S IN *TERRIBLE* TROUBLE. HE CAN'T AFFORD A LAWYER. WHAT WILL WE DO?

MRS. PARKER? MATT MURDOCK-- I COULDN'T HELP BUT OVERHEAR.

YES, *THAT* MATT MURDOCK. MRS. PARKER, A LAWYER WILL BE PROVIDED *FREE* FOR MR. POPCHIK.

NO, IT WON'T BE ME. BUT I'LL HELP TO SEE HE GETS THE FAIREST SHAKE POSSIBLE. I'D LIKE TO PROVE TO YOUR NEPHEW HERE THAT THE SYSTEM WORKS.

I'LL KEEP AN OPEN MIND.

THAT'S ALL I ASK, PETER. NOW, MRS. PARKER, AS I WAS SAYING-- CAN I CALL YOU MAY--?

PETER DAVID
writer

RICH BUCKLER
layouts

M. HANDS
finishers

BOB SHAREN
colorist

RICK PARKER
letterer

JIM OWSLEY
editor

JIM SHOOTER
editor-in-chief

THERE GOES THE D.A.'S CASE-- UP IN SMOKE!

THAT'S ROUGH! REMIND ME TO CRY *LATER!*

--HIGH OCTANE!

MR. TREECE? CHANCE HERE. I'M HAPPY TO REPORT THAT I'VE WON OUR WAGER-- *ORIN CONCARD!* WON'T BE TESTIFYING AGAINST YOU!

I'LL BE BY TO PICK UP MY $10,000 MOMENTARILY!

A SATISFIED SMILE BLOSSOMING BENEATH HIS PENCIL-THIN MUS-TACHE, CHANCE ROCKETS SOUTH TOWARD MANHATTAN--

--PASSING HIGH OVER *THE CLOISTERS*--

--BUILDINGS OF ANCIENT ELEGANCE CURRENTLY SERVING AS A BACKDROP FOR MORE *MODERN* BEAUTY--

--IN THE FORM OF FASHION MODEL *MARY JANE WATSON-PARKER.*

THAT'S FABULOUS! *SUPER!* JUST A COUPLE MORE ROLLS--

CLICK! WHIRRR!

"-- AND WE CAN CALL IT--

CLICK
WHRRR
CLICK
WHRRR
CLICK

"-- A WRAP!"

GREAT STUFF, KID! THE LENS LOVES YA! GOT TIME FOR A STUDIO SHOOT NEXT WEEK?

DON'T KNOW, HAL. I'LL CHECK WITH MY AGENCY.

AND SOON...

WHEW! I LOVE THE WORK, BUT I'M EXHAUSTED!

I CAN SYMPATHIZE. I'M POOPED FROM JUST FIXING YOUR HAIR ALL DAY!

YOU DO A TERRIFIC JOB, SANDY. THANKS!

GUESS I'D BETTER GIVE PETER A CALL NOW. LET HIM KNOW I'LL BE LATE--

--AT 410 CHELSEA STREET...

PETER AND MARY JANE ARE BUSY RIGHT NOW--

--BUT IF YOU'LL LEAVE A MESSAGE AT THE TONE, WE'LL GET BACK TO YOU SOON.

HI. IT'S ME. WE HAVE A CHANCE TO GET THAT CONDO IN THE BEDFORD TOWERS, HON.

BOY, MARRIED LIFE SURE IS AN ADJUSTMENT! SOMETIMES I FEEL LIKE I'M BACK IN SCHOOL, HAVING TO REPORT TO MOM ALL THE TIME!

'COURSE, HAVING A "MOM" AS CUTE AS PETER DOES MAKE IT EASIER TO TAKE!

CHELSE

BEEP

HOWEVER, AS CONNECTIONS ARE MADE.

I'M GOING TO CHECK IT OUT ON MY WAY HOME. LOVE YOU. 'BYE.

HOURS LATER. THE DAILY BUGLE BUILDING, HOME OF NEW YORK'S CRUSADING DAILY NEWSPAPER, WHERE FREE-LANCE PHOTOGRAPHER PETER PARKER RETRIEVES A RECORDED MESSAGE...

--HOME. LOVE YOU. 'BYE.

NUTS.

PROBLEMS, PETER?

SORT OF. LOOKS LIKE I MAY BE MOVING INTO THE *BEDFORD TOWERS*, ROBBIE.

THAT'S A *PROBLEM?* THE BEDFORD'S THE CLASSIEST BUILDING ON THE WEST SIDE!

I KNOW. IT'S GOOD FOR MARY JANE'S IMAGE. BESIDES-- --WE REALLY DO NEED A BIGGER PLACE.

FORGIVE ME FOR ASKING, PETE, BUT CAN YOU *AFFORD* THE BEDFORD?

ARE YOU KIDDING? I CAN BARELY AFFORD THE *YMCA!*

BUT I GUESS THERE ARE ADVANTAGES TO HAVING A WIFE WHO MAKES MORE MONEY THAN *IBM!*

I, UM, DON'T SUPPOSE YOU HAVE ANY PHOTO ASSIGNMENTS TO HAND OUT?

SORRY, PETE. NOTHING CURRENT. BUT I'LL KEEP YOU IN MIND.

NEVERTHELESS, AFTER A SHORT, AFFORDABLE WEB-SWING TO CHELSEA STREET--

-- SPIDER-MAN'S SPIDER-SENSE ASSURES HIM THAT NO ONE IS WATCHING--

-- AND HE DROPS THROUGH A ROOFTOP SKYLIGHT INTO THE COMFORTABLE CHAOS HE CALLS--

--"HOME."

WHAT A MESS!

THIS PLACE WAS SMALL EVEN *BEFORE* MARY JANE MOVED SOME OF HER STUFF IN! AND NOW-- HEY, WHAT AM *I* COMPLAINING ABOUT?

MJ'S BEEN COMPLETELY *UPROOTED!* SHE'S TRYING TO KEEP HER CAREER GOING WHILE LIVING OUT OF BOXES, AND ALL I THINK OF IS *ME!*

I SHOULD DO SOMETHING FOR HER, TO LIFT HER SPIRITS. SOMETHING CRAZY...UNEXPECTED..

... DUMB.

HMMM...

WITH APOLOGIES TO THAT GUY IN PYGMALION--

--"I THINK I'VE *GOT* IT!"

--AND A DELICATE HAND FITS A KEY INTO A RABSON DEADBOLT LOCK...

SHLIK

PETER? IT'S ME-- HUH?

PETER?!

BONE-SWAR, MUH-DAM! YOUR CHICKEN MAC-NOO-GEETS ARE READY! AND FOR DEE-ZAIRT... ﹩HAW-HAW﹩...

...ZE *YOU-ZYU-ELL?*

UHHH, PETER--

--I-I BROUGHT *SANDY* HOME TO MEET YOU.

HI!

EEP!

UH, H-HELLO, THERE!

S-S-SO NICE TO BE MET!'ER--

--'SCUSE ME?

SLAM

OH, MARY JANE. HE *IS* CUTE!

UH-HUH.

AND GOOD FOR A FEW LAUGHS, TOO!

WHILE AT THAT MOMENT, IN FRONT OF THE WORLD-FAMOUS *HEARTH* RESTAURANT...

THAT WAS WONDERFUL, NICHOLAS. SO FEW MODERN MEN KNOW HOW TO TREAT A *LADY.*

THE DELIGHT, DEAR STEPHANIE, WAS ENTIRELY MY OWN. I--

--AH. HOW UNFORTUNATE. MY WRIST ALARM.

BEEP BEEP

THE *PAGING* TONE.

OH, POO.

I'M SORRY, DARLING. I LEFT INSTRUCTIONS NOT TO BE BOTHERED UNLESS IT WAS *EXTREMELY* IMPORTANT. I'LL CALL YOU TOMORROW. YOUR HUSBAND *WILL* STILL BE IN MADRID?

HERE, YOU TAKE THE LIMO, I'LL GET A--

--TAXI!!

I'D LIKE TO BE AT RIVERSIDE AND 73RD IN FIVE MINUTES, MY GOOD MAN. BUT I DOUBT THIS VEHICLE IS CAPABLE OF SUCH A FEAT.

WANNA BET?

AS A MATTER OF FACT...

I DO.

VRRROOOM

AND, 41½ MINUTES LATER, AT THE EXCLUSIVE PENT-HOUSE RESIDENCE OF ONE NICHOLAS POWELL...

WIN A FEW, LOSE A FEW. STILL--

--THE $500 I LOST TO THAT CABBY WAS NOTHING. NOT WHEN COMPARED TO THE PULSE-QUICKENING THRILL OF THE GAMBLE ITSELF!

FOR LIFE IS DULL AT BEST, AND IS MADE TOLERABLE ONLY BY RISK. THE GREATER THE RISK, THE GREATER THE WORTH.

THE GREATER THE VERY APPRECIATION OF LIVING.

THAT'S WHY I NEVER CHARGE FOR MY SERVICES. RATHER, I WAGER THEM AGAINST MY SUCCESS.

AND THAT'S WHY I ORIGINALLY BECAME--

FLIP

--CHANCE!

CODE 6-4-7: TRACE AND CONTACT MOST RECENT CALLER.

SECONDS PASS; ELECTRICITY HUMS. THEN...

SO GOOD OF YOU TO RETURN MY CALL, MISTER... AH... "CHANCE."

I'M CARLTON DRAKE, AND I HEAD AN ORGANIZATION CALLED "THE LIFE FOUNDATION." A CERTAIN MR. TREECE SAID YOU MIGHT BE ABLE TO HELP US WITH A LITTLE PROBLEM. A...

...$20,000 PROBLEM?

MY FAVORITE KIND.

WHERE SHALL WE MEET?

THE EVENING AGES, GROWING SLOWLY INTO FULL NIGHT. WHILE IN A CLUTTERED LIVING ROOM ON CHELSEA STREET...

IT WAS REALLY GREAT MEETING YOU, PETER. NOW I HAVE SOMEONE TO PICTURE WHEN MARY JANE TALKS ABOUT YOU.

JUST PICTURE HIM *WITH* THE ROBE, OKAY, SAN?

WELL, I'LL *TRY.* LISTEN, GOOD LUCK ON GETTING INTO THE *TOWERS.* LET ME KNOW, HUH?

SURE, SANDY. I'LL CALL YOU NEXT WEEK.

G'NIGHT.

NOW, "MONSIEUR," WHAT WAS THAT ABOUT... *DESSERT?*

AW-HAW! ZE PREETY MUH-DAM HAS ZE SHARP MEE-MO-REE, NAW?

BUT OF COORZ, WE HAF SOMEZING SPECIAL ON ZE MENU TONIGHT. SOMEZING JUST FOR *VOUS.*

EET EES CALLED...

...ZE VENUS *BUTTERFLY!*

OOO. I'LL TAKE *TWO.*

PLAMP

UPTOWN.

MISTER MACVAY?

THE ENDICOTT BUILDING.

AYE?

WHERE THE BOARD OF DIRECTORS OF *THE LIFE FOUNDATION* HOLDS A CLOSED-DOOR SESSION.

AM I TO UNDERSTAND THAT YOU HAVE *QUALMS* CONCERNING MY CHOICE OF AN OPERATIVE?

THAT I HAVE, SAR. THIS *CHANCE* LADDIE FITS OUR NEEDS, A'RIGHT, BUT HE'S A WEE BIT *FLASHY* FER ME.

OUR CURRENT VENTURE COULD FAIR BE COMPROMISED IF'N TOO MUCH *ATTENTION* WAS TO BE DRAWN TO IT!

POINT TAKEN, MR. MACVAY. BUT CHANCE COMES HIGHLY RECOMMENDED, FOR HIS EFFICIENCY AS WELL AS HIS PROFESSIONALISM.

I BELIEVE WE CAN TRUST HIM TO EXERCISE THE PROPER DEGREE OF, SHALL WE SAY--

--*SUB*TLETY?

TAP TAP TAP

WHAT THE--?

GOTT IM HIMMEL!

GOOD EVENING! I HOPE YOU DON'T MIND THE RATHER *NONSTANDARD* ENTRANCE.

BUT I'VE FOUND THAT DOORMEN AND SECURITY GUARDS CAN BE MOST ANNOYING WHEN PLACED ON A *WITNESS STAND.*

THESE WINDOWS *DO* OPEN?

YOUR CONSIDERATION IS ADMIRABLE. WE WERE JUST DISCUSSING THE NEED FOR *RESTRAINT.*

YOU MUST BE *DRAKE.*

I'M *CHANCE.*

SO I GATHERED. I'LL GET TO THE POINT, SIR: TOMORROW EVENING, AT PIER 17, A SECRET SHIPMENT OF EURO-ARMS WILL ARRIVE. WE WANT YOU TO *STEAL* IT FOR US.

THAT'S TOO BAD. I MAY BE A MURDERER, BUT I HAVE MY STANDARDS.

I DON'T WORK FOR *TERRORISTS.*

REALLY, DO WE LOOK LIKE *HEATHENS?* THE ARMS ARE TO BE USED EXCLUSIVELY FOR DEFENSE, WITH NO CIVILIANS INVOLVED. MR. TREECE WILL VOUCH FOR OUR HONESTY, AS WELL AS OUR WAGER OF OF--

--TWENTY-*FIVE* THOUSAND DOLLARS?

OH. THAT'S *DIFFERENT.*

YOU'RE ON!

SHHHROW

MS. CAPUTO, IN THE EVENT THAT CHANCE IS *SUCCESSFUL*--

--DO REMEMBER TO DEDUCT THE PRICE OF A NEW *CARPET* FROM HIS FEE, WON'T YOU?

A DAY PASSES, FILLED WITH STORIES TO BE TOLD ANOTHER TIME.

AND AS A NEW NIGHT SETTLES OVER THE HUDSON RIVER, A VOLATILE CARGO IS TRANSFERRED FROM SHIP TO SHORE UNDER THE CAREFUL GAZE OF AN ELITE MILITARY GUARD.

WHILE NEARBY, AN UNAUTHORIZED PAIR OF EYES WATCHES THE WATCHERS...

JOY'S INFO WAS RIGHT ON THE MONEY! I'LL WAIT UNTIL A FEW MORE CRATES HAVE BEEN UNLOADED, THEN TAKE SNAPS OF--

--OH, NO! SPIDER-SENSE TINGLING! WARNING OF--

"--DANGER!"

SHRROW

WHAT THE--?!

KA-BOOM!

CHANCE!

SO MUCH FOR CASUAL OBSERVING! GOT TO WEB MY AUTOMATIC CAMERA IN POSITION--

--AND TAKE MORE *DIRECT* ACTION! YOU'D THINK I'D *READ* MORE NEWSPAPERS, SINCE I *WORK* FOR ONE! BUT I DIDN'T EVEN KNOW CHANCE WAS OUT OF JAIL!*

LOOKS LIKE IT'S UP TO ME TO PUT HIM *BACK*!

* SEE *WEB* # 15. --J.S.

HOWEVER, BEFORE SPIDER-MAN CAN ACT...

GUESS I'VE MILKED THE ELEMENT OF SURPRISE FOR ALL IT'S WORTH! NOW FOR--

--PHASE TWO!

YOU APPEAR TO BE THE RANKING OFFICER, CAPTAIN! ALLOW ME TO EXPLAIN YOUR PREDICAMENT:

WHAT MY POWER-BLAST IS DOING TO THAT RADAR TOWER, IT WILL NEXT DO TO AN *AMMO CRATE*!

THE *SHRAPNEL* ALONE WILL SLAUGHTER HALF YOUR MEN!

AMMUNITION

CEASE FIRE!

UNLESS, OF COURSE, YOU CHOOSE TO *COOPERATE*.

THAT'S AN *ORDER*!

WISE DECISION-- *WEST POINT*?

ALL RIGHT, JULIO. YOU MAY SURFACE NOW.

A SUBMARINE?! WOW. WHOEVER'S FINANCING THIS OPERATION MUST BE LOADED! AND NOW THAT I THINK OF IT--

-- MAYBE I CAN TURN THIS INTO SOME EXTRA MONEY *MYSELF!* I MEAN, I'VE ALREADY *GOT* SHOTS OF CHANCE STEALING THE MUNITIONS.

IT'S KIND OF RISKY, BUT CHANCE ONLY KILLS PEOPLE HE'S *HIRED* TO KILL. SO ALL I SHOULD HAVE TO DO IS SIT TIGHT, AND HOPE NOTHING GOES --

IF I LET HIM GO, THEN FOLLOW HIM AND TAKE PICTURES OF *SPIDER-MAN* GETTING THE WEAPONS *BACK*, I COULD SELL *TWO* STORIES AND *DOUBLE* MY PAYCHECK!

-- WRONG? TH-THE LIGHTS! THEY'VE *ALL* GONE OUT! B-BUT NEW YORK HASN'T HAD A *BLACKOUT* IN OVER A DECADE!*

* FOR AN EXPLANATION OF *THIS* ONE, SEE X-FACTOR #25. --J.S.

JUST TAKE IT EASY, SPIDEY! EMERGENCY GENERATORS SHOULD KICK IN SOON! E-EVERYTHING WILL BE OKAY AS LONG AS NO ONE DOES ANYTHING--

"--STUPID!"

NOW'S MY CHANCE! GOT TO GET TO MY RIFLE BEFORE--

REALLY, YOU'D THINK THEY'D *ASSUME* MY HELMET SCANS IN *INFRARED!*

FRANK!

UNG!

WHA--

--N--

-- NOOOOOO!

SPIDER-MAN?

MOVING FASTER THAN MY TARGETING COMPUTERS CAN TRACK!

CHANCE!

YOU'RE *MINE!*

SLAVERY, SPIDER-MAN? IN THIS DAY AND AGE?

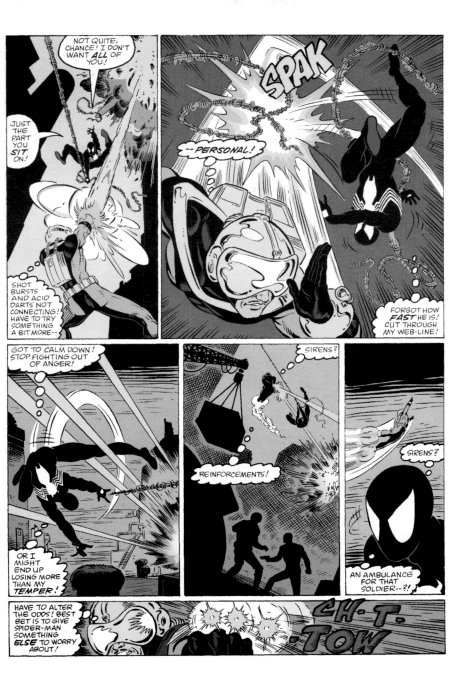

SPIDER-MAN BROODS. MIDNIGHT ARRIVES. WHILE AT THE ENDICOTT BUILDING, PRIVATE POWER SUPPLIES PUSH BACK THE DARKNESS...

... SO THAT BUSINESS MIGHT PROCEED AS USUAL.

A *CASH RECEIPT?* MR. DRAKE, I DOUBT MANY BANKS WOULD HONOR *MY* SIGNATURE!

A MATTER OF INTERNAL BOOKKEEPING. A MERE *FORMALITY.*

IF YOU'D BE SO KIND...?

ALL RIGHT. FOR $25,000 I MIGHT AS WELL HUMOR Y--

--*EEYIIIHII!!*

THAT PEN WAS A GOOD *CONDUCTOR,* SIR. HE'S OUT... BUT STILL *ALIVE.*

GOOD. THEN THE CHARGE IN THE *STUN PLATE* WAS ADEQUATELY CALIBRATED. AFTER ALL, WE DON'T WANT MR. CHANCE *DEAD.* AT LEAST--

--NOT *YET.*

ELSEWHERE, UNSUNG HEROES STRUGGLE TO RESTORE POWER TO THE GREATEST CITY ON EARTH.

BUT WITHIN THAT CITY, ANOTHER HERO STRUGGLES WITH A FOE HE CAN *NEVER* ESCAPE.

HIMSELF.

I STILL CAN'T BELIEVE WHAT I DID. THAT I LEFT PEOPLE IN *DANGER* JUST TO MAKE A FEW EXTRA DOLLARS.

I CAN'T BELIEVE IT, EITHER. I CAN'T BELIEVE YOU THOUGHT SO POORLY OF *ME!*

NAGEL

HUH?

DO YOU REALLY THINK MONEY MEANS THAT *MUCH* TO ME? THAT I *CARE* HOW MUCH YOU'VE GOT? PETER, *YOU'RE* WHAT'S IMPORTANT IN MY LIFE! YOU MAKE ME HAPPY. AND HAPPINESS DOESN'T COME WITH A *PRICE TAG.*

I... I *KNOW* THAT. BUT KNOWING SOMETHING, AND *FEELING* IT, AREN'T ALWAYS THE SAME THING.

THEN I GUESS WE'LL JUST HAVE TO WORK A LITTLE HARDER, HUH, TIGER?

YEAH...

...I GUESS WE WILL.

THAT'S WHEN I DECIDED TO *FOLLOW* THE TRUCK, TO CATCH CHANCE WITH THE GOODS!

BUT I DIDN'T COUNT ON THIS TRAFFIC JAM-- *OR* ON A KID WITH A *MOUTH* AS BIG AS THE HOLLAND TUNNEL!

ALL RIGHT, YOU! GET DOWN!

AND JUST BECAUSE I'M IN A GOOD MOOD TODAY--

--I'M GOING TO LET *YOU* ARREST HIM!

THE CREEP'S BLOWIN' SMOKE, OFFICER. I'M JUST HAULIN' BUILDIN' SUPPLIES.

FOR *CARLTON DRAKE.*

PERFECT...

THAT'S BIG O'YA.

UM, YOU MAY FIND THIS HARD TO BELIEVE, OFFICER, BUT THERE'S A *MASTER CRIMINAL* INSIDE THIS TRUCK!

WHAT'S *YOUR* STORY, DRIVER?

DRAKE? THE WALL STREET BIGWIG?

YOU'D BETTER HAVE *PROOF* WEBSLINGER!

BLAST! I COULD RIP THE DOORS OFF THE VAN AND SHOW HIM, BUT CHANCE MIGHT COME OUT *SHOOTING!*

I, UH, DON'T SUPPOSE YOU'D TAKE MY *WORD?*

THAT DOES IT! MOVE IT OUT, DRIVER! AND AS FOR *YOU,* HOTSHOT--

--NEXT TIME GET YER *FACTS* STRAIGHT!

AMMO

AMMO

AMMO

AMMO

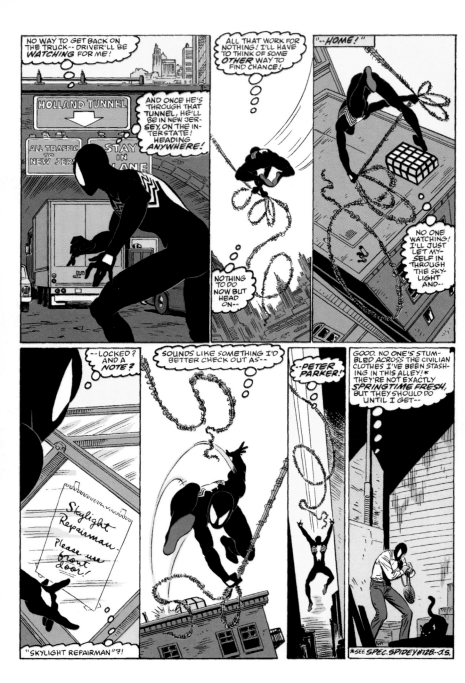

AT THAT MOMENT, PETER PARKER FINDS BRIGHT LIGHTS AND HOT SOUNDS DEFINITELY APPEALING.

BUT AS DUSK LOWERS OVER NORTHERN *NEW JERSEY,* THE ONLY LIGHTS SEEN THERE COME FROM A 16-WHEELER PULLING UP TO A HEAVILY-GUARDED GATE, WHILE THE ONLY SOUNDS--

-- ARE THOSE OF *CONSPIRACY!*

LOOKS PEACEFUL, DOESN'T HE?

MAYBE NOW, MR. DRAKE. BUT WHEN *CHANCE* WAKES UP AND FINDS WE NEVER INTENDED TO *PAY* HIM FOR THOSE WEAPONS, THAT WE *TRICKED* HIM INTO BEING OUR PRISONER--

-- HE COULD BE TROUBLE!

MR. GABRIEL, YOU'VE BEEN A BOARD MEMBER OF *THE LIFE FOUNDATION* FOR YEARS, YOU SHOULD KNOW BY NOW--

--THAT WE PREPARE FOR *ANY* EVENTUALITY. LIKE IT OR NOT, CHANCE *WILL* BE A KEY ELEMENT--

--IN OUR BOLDEST, MOST *PROFITABLE* VENTURE EVER:

SANCTUM MAXIMUS!

WHILE IN NEW YORK, THE NIGHT GROWS OLD--

THE UNDEAD Club

STOP SQUIRMING, PETER! YOU ACT LIKE YOUR *MOTHER* DRESSED YOU, NOT ME!

SORRY, MJ. I'LL TRY TO LOOK COOL, ER, *HOT!*

WHATEVER...

OH, LOOK! THERE'S EDDIE! *HI, EDDIE!*

THE *COMEDIAN?* YOU *KNOW* HIM?!?

SURE. HE'S A REAL SWEETHEART.

ONCE YOU GET PAST HIS *BODYGUARDS!*

POKE!

EMJAY! WE'VE JUST *GOTTA* HAVE ONE NUTTY LITTLE DANCE!

PAUL! GOOD TO SEE YOU!

-- AND BECOMES THE PROPERTY OF THE YOUNG.

I *HEARD* YOU TIED THE KNOT. THIS MUST BE THE LUCKY CAT!

UH-HUH. WOULD YOU MIND, PETER?

UH, NO! GO RIGHT AHEAD!

THANKS, BABE.

WOW. I MAY NEVER FIT INTO MARY JANE'S WORLD COMPLETELY--

--BUT IT SURE IS A FUN PLACE TO *VISIT* ONCE IN A WHILE!

NEW JERSEY: CONSTRUCTION CONTINUES ON WHAT APPEARS TO BE A SMALL CITY HIDDEN BENEATH A GARGANTUAN CAMOUFLAGED DOME.

WHILE INSIDE ONE OF THE COMPLETED BUILDINGS...

WE BROUGHT YOU HERE IN ORDER TO DUPLICATE YOUR *WRIST BLASTERS* AND *ANKLE JETS.* HOWEVER, OUR SCIENTISTS CAN'T SEEM TO FIND ANY *TRIGGER* MECHANISMS.

THEY'RE OBVIOUSLY ACTIVATED *CYBERNETICALLY,* BUT WE HAVEN'T BEEN ABLE TO DISCOVER THE PRECISE METHOD.

OUR RESOURCES ARE VAST. YOU WOULD BE WISE TO TELL US EXACTLY WHAT WE WANT TO KNOW... WHILE YOU'RE STILL RELATIVELY *UNDAMAGED.* FOR I ASSURE YOU, ONE WAY OR ANOTHER--

YOU ARE A UNIQUE INDIVIDUAL, CHANCE. A CRIMINAL-FOR-HIRE WHO DOES NOT *CHARGE* FOR HIS SERVICES. RATHER, YOU *WAGER* YOUR FEE AGAINST YOUR SUCCESS. TO YOU, *RISK* IS ALL.

NEVER-THELESS, I SUGGEST YOU CONSIDER THE UNFAVORABLE *ODDS* INHERENT IN YOUR PRESENT SITUATION.

--YOU *WILL* TELL US.

WANNA *BET?*

CHELSEA STREET: AN EARLY-MORNING MOON SHINES INTO A TOP FLOOR APARTMENT.

WHERE A COUPLE, NEWLY WED, LIES EASY AND TALKS, AS NEWLY-WEDS ARE WONT TO DO...

THE CLUB WAS FABULOUS, MARY JANE, AND I'D LIKE TO DO IT AGAIN SOME TIME. BUT NOW THE MUSIC'S STOPPED AND REALITY'S STILL HERE.

I KNOW THAT SOMEWHERE, SOMEONE'S GOT A SHIPMENT OF STOLEN MILITARY WEAPONS--

DIDN'T WORK, HUH, TIGER?

-- AND I CAN'T HELP WORRYING ABOUT WHAT'S GOING TO BE DONE WITH THEM... WHO'S GOING TO BE KILLED WITH THEM.

I JUST CAN'T RUN AWAY FROM IT. SOMEHOW, I'VE GOT TO FIND CHANCE!

I..., I UNDERSTAND, PETER. JUST...

...BE CAREFUL, OKAY?

MANHATTAN: NEW SUN BRIGHTENS THE DOWNTOWN SKYSCRAPER SERVING AS HEADQUARTERS FOR THE CITY'S HARDEST-WORKING NEWSPAPER.

DAILY·BUGLE

AN INSTITUTION WHOSE BACK-ISSUE "MORGUE" CURRENTLY FUNCTIONS AS A RESEARCH MECCA FOR ONE PETER PARKER...

MY ONLY CLUE IS THE NAME, *"CARLTON DRAKE."* I'VE READ EVERYTHING WRITTEN ABOUT THE MAN IN THE LAST FEW YEARS, BUT HAVEN'T FOUND ANYTHING EVEN VAGUELY *SINISTER.*

THERE WERE HINTS OF POLITICAL MANIPULATION, INSIDER STOCK DEALS, THE USUAL STUFF YOU FIND ABOUT MOST WEALTHY, POWERFUL MEN --

-- BUT THE ONLY OUT-OF-THE-ORDINARY ITEM WAS THE WITH-DRAWAL OF SUPPORT FOR AN AGRICULTURAL RESEARCH PROJECT AT EMPIRE STATE UNIVERSITY.

THANKS, EARL.

SURE THING, PETE.

AND THE ONLY THING STRANGE ABOUT THAT WAS THAT IT HAD BEEN A VALUABLE TAX WRITE-OFF -- AND NO *REASON* WAS GIVEN FOR THE WITHDRAWAL!

EXCUSE ME A MINUTE, MS. THOMPSON.

PETER! HAVEN'T SEEN YOU AROUND FOR AWHILE. HEADING OUT TO GET US SOME MORE FREELANCE PHOTOS?

MAYBE LATER, ROBBIE. RIGHT NOW --

-- I'M GOING BACK TO *SCHOOL!*

EMPIRE STATE UNIVERSITY: ONE OF NEW YORK'S FOREMOST INSTITUTES OF HIGHER LEARNING.

E.S.U. CAMPUS

AND A SOURCE OF FOND NOSTALGIA FOR PETER PARKER. HE REMEMBERS HIS UNDERGRADUATE DAYS, THE CAREFREE LIFE, THE EXCITEMENT OF DISCOVERY.

THUS HIS SMILE IS BOTH GENUINE AND WIDE AS HE ENTERS THE REGISTRAR'S OFFICE--

-- AND SHARES THAT SMILE WITH ADMINISTRATIVE ASSISTANT, **ANNIE DEITZ**...

I'VE CALLED UP THE INFORMATION YOU WANTED, PETER. BUT SINCE YOU AREN'T A **STUDENT** ANYMORE, YOU'RE NOT SUPPOSED TO **LOOK** AT IT.

I HOPE YOU'LL REMEMBER THAT WHILE I'M OFF POWDERING MY NOSE. FOR, SAY, **FIVE MINUTES?**

ADMINISTRATION

THANKS, ANNIE.

DO NOT OVER FILL

AND, ONCE ALONE...

HMM. THE SUPPORT DRAKE WITHDREW WAS A **RENT-FREE LEASE.**

ON SEVERAL HUNDRED ACRES OF PRIME FOREST LAND-- --IN NORTHERN **NEW JERSEY!** AND JERSEY WAS WHERE THAT SHIPMENT OF "BUILDING SUPPLIES" WAS HEADED!

BETTER CALL MARY JANE.

-- NO. SHE'D JUST WORRY.

I'LL TELL HER LATER.

LET HER KNOW I'LL BE LATE FOR--

STATE ROAD 62: A NORTH-BOUND TRUCKER RELEASES A LONE HITCH-HIKER TO THE NEW JERSEY WILDERNESS.

A TRAVELER WHO THEN TURNS AND CAUTIOUSLY ENTERS THE TWILIGHT-DIMMED WOODLANDS...

BUS GOT ME TO THE NEAREST TOWN. HAD TO THUMB MY WAY HERE, THOUGH. SHOULD BE CLOSE TO THE AREA SHOWN IN THE E.S.U. RECORDS. I JUST HOPE--

--WHOA! EITHER THIS IS A FACTORY OUTLET FOR "GUARDS A-US," OR I'VE HIT THE JACKPOT!

TIME TO GO TO WORK...

THWIP

"--CHANCE!"

PINGK
PINGK
PINGK

...WE WERE ROLLIN' THE BONES... LIKE OLD GAMBLERS DO... ♪ TOSSIN' THE CUBES... ♪ TILL QUARTER TO TWO... ♪

HUH...?

OKAY, CHANCE, WHAT'S GOING ON?

SPIDER-MAN! HOW NICE OF YOU TO DROP IN! AND WHAT A CLEVER PLOY, GAINING ACCESS THROUGH A VENTILATION SHAFT!

THE CONTROLS FOR MY SHACKLES ARE ON THAT CONSOLE SOMEWHERE. RELEASE ME, DEAR BOY--

--AND I'LL TELL YOU EVERYTHING!

WITHOUT WEAPONS, CHANCE IS NO THREAT! BESIDES, I DON'T HAVE TIME TO BARGAIN!

OKAY! TALK!

BASICALLY, I'VE FOUND THAT DRAKE AND THE LIFE FOUNDATION ARE SURVIVALISTS-- BUT A VERY SPECIAL BREED!

THOUGH THEY FEEL THAT THE WORLD MAY SOON PLUNGE INTO TOTAL CHAOS, THEY HAVE NO INTEREST IN LIVING OFF THE LAND, ROUGHING IT, THAT SORT OF THING.

AND THEY'RE CONVINCED THERE ARE OTHERS WHO WANT TO SURVIVE, BUT DON'T WANT TO WORK FOR IT. SO THEY'VE SET UP THIS SURVIVAL COMMUNITY, COMPLETE WITH EVERY LUXURY FROM SWIMMING POOLS TO SAUNAS--

--AND THEY'RE SELLING ESCAPE CONDOS TO THE RICH AND FAMOUS FOR FIVE MILLION A POP!

FOR PROTECTION, THEY HIRED A PRIVATE ARMY AND EQUIPPED THEM WITH WEAPONS THEY HAD ME STEAL! BUT THERE WAS A HITCH: BEING THE ONLY ONES ARMED, THOSE "PROTECTORS" MIGHT DECIDE TO *TAKE OVER!*

SO THE LIFE FOUNDATION THOUGHT TO EQUIP *THEM-SELVES* WITH MY WRIST BLASTERS!

TO POLICE THE POLICE, SO TO SPEAK!

RATHER BRILLIANT, MAKING CALAMITY *PAY* LIKE THAT. TOO BAD THEY DIDN'T JUST *ASK* FOR MY HELP.

I MIGHT'VE BOUGHT IN...!

YEAH...

..WELL...

...AHHHH...

...*PHOOEY!*

TOK

TOK

TOK

TOK

TOK

KLIK

REEEEEEEEEEEEEE

IT WORKED! BUT THE RELEASE SEQUENCE MUST HAVE BEEN *CODED!* SET OFF AN ALARM! HAVE TO GET TO MY BLASTERS!

HOLD IT, CHANCE! THAT WASN'T PART OF THE *DEAL!*

INTRUDER! SHOOT TO KILL!

NEITHER WERE *THEY,* SPIDER-MAN. TRUCE?

NUTS!

TRUCE!

SNAP!

BOOM BOOM

SOME TIME LATER, AS THE SOUND OF SIRENS DRAWS NEAR...

YEAH, I GUESS. AT LEAST THOSE **GUNS** WON'T KILL ANY **INNOCENTS**.

AND THE SECRET OF MY WEAPONS SYSTEM **REMAINS** A SECRET!

THANKS FOR YOUR HELP, SPIDER-MAN. OF COURSE, THAT WON'T CHANGE THINGS WHEN WE MEET **WITHOUT** A TRUCE, BUT AT LEAST LET ME OFFER YOU A LIFT BACK TO MANHATTAN.

HMM. MARY JANE COULD BE GETTING ANXIOUS. BUS IS KINDA SLOW.

I ACCEPT!

THAT WAS KIND OF **EXTREME**, CHANCE!

PERHAPS. BUT IT **WORKED!**

HOWEVER...

YEESH! I- I FIGURED HE HAD A **CAR** STASHED SOMEWHERE! I'M NOT USED TO FLYING WITHOUT **WEBS!**

SURE HOPE MARY JANE **APPRECIATES** THIS!

Stan Lee PROUDLY PRESENTS A COMIC BOOK MILESTONE: THE FABULOUS 300TH ISSUE OF...

THE AMAZING SPIDER-MAN®

VENOM

HER NAME IS *MARY JANE WATSON-PARKER*.

BUT SHE DOESN'T KNOW THAT.

AT THIS MOMENT, SHE KNOWS ALMOST *NOTHING*.

FOR HER MIND HAS BEEN HARSHLY NUMBED, ALL THOUGHT CRUELLY DROWNED IN AN ONRUSHING TIDE OF PRIMAL *FEAR.*

AN EMOTION THAT MAY *NEVER* FULLY FADE...

DON'T COME NEAR ME! P-PLEASE! D-DON'T *TOUCH ME!!*

DAVID MICHELINIE — WRITER

TODD McFARLANE — ART

RICK PARKER — LETTERS

BOB SHAREN — COLOR

JIM SALICRUP — EDITOR

TOM DeFALCO — EDITOR IN CHIEF

ANSWER: THE KIND THAT CURRENTLY CRAWLS UP THE SHEER WALL OF A SOUTH BRONX TENEMENT. THE KIND THAT HAS JUST COME--

-- HOME.

YEAH, YEAH, I KNOW! THE *WOMAN* WASN'T OUR TARGET! BUT SHAKING HER UP COULD STILL WORK! I MEAN, IF WE DON'T FIND *HIM*--

--*HE* MIGHT FIND *US!* EITHER WAY--

--IT'S JUST...

...A MATTER...

...OF TIME!

GUESS I'LL PUMP A LITTLE IRON. POP A SWEAT. YOU MAY NOT GET YOUR POWER FROM MUSCLE BUDDY, BUT *I* SURE DO!

AND I WANT TO MAKE CERTAIN I'M IN SHAPE, Y'KNOW?

FOR THE KILL!

HIH HIH

AN ALIEN WHO WANTED ME FOR ITS *HOST,* WHO EVEN TRIED TO *BOND* ITSELF TO MY BODY!

"IT FINALLY TOOK MR. FANTASTIC'S *SONIC BLASTER* TO CAPTURE THE CREATURE!

"BUT IT ESCAPED, DETERMINED TO JOIN WITH ME *PERMANENTLY.* I GOT DESPERATE.

"-- AND LET THE SHATTERING CLAMOR OF THE BELLS *KILL* THE MONSTER BEFORE IT COULD DESTROY *ME!*"*

"*SO* DESPERATE THAT I LURED IT TO A CHURCH TOWER--

*SEE *WEB OF SPIDER-MAN* #1.-- J.S.

BUT FROM WHAT MARY JANE SAYS, THE REPORTS OF THAT DEATH MAY HAVE BEEN SOMEWHAT... *PREMATURE!*

NUTS. I'M REALLY STRUNG TIGHT.

IN THE PAST, I'D LOOSEN UP WITH A LITTLE WEB-SWINGING, MAYBE TAKE SOME PHOTOS FOR THE *DAILY BUGLE.*

BUT I'M A MARRIED MAN NOW, AND I HAVE TO STAY WITH MARY JANE UNTIL --

¿ *NNNNN...* ¿ PETER?

COME TO BED.

I THINK I KNOW WHO TERRORIZED YOU, M.J. AND WHY THEY'RE AFTER SPIDER-MAN. I HOPED MY HAVING A *SECRET IDENTITY* WOULD SHIELD YOU, BUT--

HUSH, TIGER. WHEN I SIGNED ON "FOR BETTER OR FOR WORSE," I *MEANT* IT.

NOW LET'S GET SOME SLEEP, OKAY?

[151]

STUBBORNLY, GRUDGINGLY, FITFUL SLEEP FINALLY COMES.

AND EVENTUALLY, AS THE SUN SLIPS INTO ITS ASSIGNED POSITION OVER MANHATTAN ONCE MORE...

ERRNNGG... ＞YAWN＜ MARY JANE...?

OVER HERE, PETER.

I HOPE YOU WEREN'T CALLING ROOM SERVICE-- I ALREADY KNOW WHAT I WANT FOR BREAKFAST!

SILLY. I WAS CALLING A REAL ESTATE AGENT I KNOW. I'VE PULLED IN SOME MARKERS--

-- AND WE'VE BEEN MOVED TO THE TOP OF THE WAITING LIST FOR THE BEDFORD TOWERS!

IF WE WANT THAT CONDO, IT'S OURS!

B-BUT, IT USUALLY TAKES MONTHS TO GET A GOOD PLACE IN MANHATTAN!

I GUESS WE WERE JUST LUCKY. I KNOW THIS IS SUDDEN, PETER, BUT I JUST CAN'T LIVE IN THAT APARTMENT ANYMORE. I'D SCREAM AT EVERY LITTLE CREAK OR RATTLE!

YOU DO UNDERSTAND... DON'T YOU?

IF I HAD A NICKEL FOR EVERY TIME I'VE DROPPED THROUGH THIS SKYLIGHT--

--MAYBE I COULD AFFORD TO PAY FOR MY SHARE OF THAT *CONDO!*

SPEAKING OF WHICH--

--I WONDER IF THERE'LL BE A PROBLEM GETTING IN AND OUT AS *SPIDER-MAN?*

GUESS I'LL SWING ACROSS *THAT* BRIDGE WHEN I COME TO IT. NOW, I'VE GOT *OTHER* THINGS TO WORRY ABOUT.

AND TO TAKE *PRECAUTIONS* AGAINST!

I BORROWED THIS SONIC BLASTER FROM THE *FANTASTIC FOUR* ON MY WAY OVER.

I JUST HOPE I DON'T HAVE TO *USE--*

--HNH? LIGHT BLINKING ON MARY JANE'S ANSWERING MACHINE. BETTER SEE WHAT IT IS.

HI, KIDS! THIS IS AUNT MAY. JUST CALLING TO REMIND YOU ABOUT DINNER TONIGHT. CHICKEN AND DUMPLINGS AT SEVEN P.M. SHORT-- I-I MEAN *SHARP!* OH, PHOOEY, I *HATE* THESE CONTRAPTIONS! ⚡CLICK⚡

HE'S DUCKING INTO AN ALLEYWAY! MUST BE A SHORT-CUT!

BLAST! NO *CROWD* TO HIDE IN! WE'D BETTER GIVE HIM A FEW SECONDS TO GET AHEAD, THEN--

WHAT--?! HE'S *GONE!*

LIVING IN NEW YORK FOR SO LONG MAY HAVE MADE ME *PARANOID*, BUT I CAN'T HELP BELIEVING THAT OLD SAYING: "BETTER SAFE--

"--THAN *SPLATTERED!*

AND THUS, A SHORT WHILE LATER, AT THE EXCLUSIVE *BEDFORD TOWERS* CONDOMINIUM RESIDENCE...

WOW.

A DAY PASSES. THE YOUNG POLICE-MAN'S BODY IS NOT FOUND.

AND AS EVENING SETTLES ONCE MORE OVER THE IMPOSING EDIFICE OF THE BEDFORD TOWERS...

SORRY THIS MOVE IS SO LATE, FOLKS. ON SUCH SHORT NOTICE, I COULDN'T GET A VAN ANY EARLIER.

NO PROBLEM, MJ.

WHOA! THAT RED-HEADED GUY'S HAIRDO IS RADICAL!

DARN! I'M MISSING THE NETS GAME! THAT MAKES ME MAD!

WHO ARE THESE PEOPLE?

I RAN OUT OF YOUR FRIENDS, PETER, SO I CALLED IN SOME OF MINE!

DO HURRY WITH THOSE BOXES, JEEVES. WATCH-ING YOU CARRY THEM IS POSITIVELY EXHAUSTING!

VERY GOOD, SIR!

WOW! THERE'RE PETE'S OLD NEIGHBORS-- CANDI, RANDI, AND BAMBI!

MAN, IF I HAD THEM LIVING NEXT DOOR, I'D NEVER MOVE--

HEY!

WATCH IT!

EASY, BOYS. DON'T HURT YOURSELVES.

AND, EVENTUALLY...

WHEW! THAT'S THE LAST ONE!

SHOOT. AND I WAS JUST GETTING *PUMPED UP!*

MAYBE THEY'LL LET YOU CARRY THE *VAN* BACK TO THE *RENTAL AGENCY,* FLASH!

COME AND GET IT!

SANDY AND I'LL BUILD SOME MORE SANDWICHES WHILE YOU GUYS WORK ON THESE. SODAS ARE IN THE FRIDGE.

DIG IN!

GIVE ANY MORE THOUGHT TO MY SUGGESTION, PETE? ABOUT GETTING OUT OF NEWS PHOTOGRAPHY?

YOU'RE THE *BUGLE'S* EDITOR IN CHIEF, ROBBIE-- HOW COULD I *NOT* TAKE YOU SERIOUSLY?

IN FACT, I'VE BEEN THINKING HOW *SCIENCE* USED TO BE MY DRIVING AMBITION. MAYBE--EH?

'SCUSE ME, ROBBIE, THERE'S SOMETHING I HAVE TO DO.

NEED ANY HELP?

NO. I THINK I'D BETTER HANDLE THIS *ALONE...!*

MY COLUMN IN THE *DAILY GLOBE* WAS READ BY MILLIONS!

I WAS A SOLID REPORTER, A RESPECTED MEMBER OF THE FOURTH ESTATE!

"AT LEAST I WAS WHEN I BEGAN WRITING A SERIES OF ARTICLES ON THE *"SIN-EATER"* MURDERS A FEW MONTHS BACK.

"IT WAS PARTLY BECAUSE OF THOSE ARTICLES THAT I WAS CONTACTED BY A *MR. EMIL GREGG,* A MAN WHO CONFESSED TO *BEING* SIN-EATER!

"PROTECTING MR. GREGG'S IDENTITY THROUGH MY RIGHTS UNDER THE FIRST AMENDMENT, I TOLD HIS STORY... INCISIVELY, COMPASSIONATELY.

"THE GLOBE'S CIRCULATION SOARED.

"BUT *PRESSURE* ALSO MOUNTED. THE POLICE INSISTED THAT I REVEAL MY SOURCE, SO THAT THEY COULD *STOP* THE MURDER SPREE. UNDER ADVICE OF COUNSEL, I FINALLY WROTE MY MASTERPIECE, ANNOUNCING GREGG AS THE SIN-EATER.*

THE DAILY GLOBE FINAL 30¢
EXCLUSIVE: SIN-EA...
REVE...

THE DAILY GLOBE FINAL 30¢
EXCLUSIVE: SIN-EATER REVEALED!

"IT WAS A SENSATION--

*THESE EVENTS OCCURRED BETWEEN THE LINES DURING *SPECTACULAR SPIDER-MAN* #107-110.-- J.S.

THAT'S IT... KEEP TALKING!

--FOR ABOUT AN HOUR-AND-A-HALF!

THAT WAS HOW LONG IT WAS BEFORE *YOU* REVEALED WHO THE *REAL* SIN-EATER WAS!

" *SOON*, THE WHOLE CITY KNEW THAT *SIN-EATER* WAS ACTUALLY POLICEMAN *STAN CARTER*-- AND THAT MY STORY WAS BASED ON THE LURID RAMBLINGS OF A COMPULSIVE CONFESSOR!

" THE *GLOBE* WAS A LAUGHING STOCK. I WAS FIRED. MY PEERS QUESTIONED MY ETHICS, SHUNNED ME. I WAS FORCED TO WRITE VENOMOUS CELEBRITY EXPOSÉS AND " I WAS KIDNAPED BY ALIENS " DRIVEL FOR SCANDAL RAGS, JUST TO EKE OUT A LIVING.

" IF YOU HADN'T BUTTED IN, NO ONE WOULD HAVE KNOWN THAT EMIL GREGG *WASN'T* THE SIN-EATER

HERO

" PERHAPS CARTER WOULD HAVE BEEN SMART AND *STOPPED* HIS KILLINGS, KNOWING HE COULD GET OFF SCOT-FREE.

" PERHAPS--

JUST A LITTLE MORE....!

--MY LIFE WOULDN'T HAVE BEEN *SHATTERED!* I MAY HAVE MADE AN ERROR IN JUDGMENT, BUT I WAS ALWAYS A GOOD JOURNALIST.

AND THE GARBAGE I WAS FORCED TO WRITE BEGAN TO ROT MY SOUL.

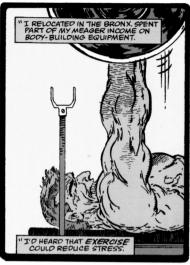

"I RELOCATED IN THE BRONX. SPENT PART OF MY MEAGER INCOME ON BODY-BUILDING EQUIPMENT.

"I'D HEARD THAT *EXERCISE* COULD REDUCE STRESS.

IT DIDN'T WORK.

"WHENEVER I LIFTED A BARBELL, IT WAS YOUR *THROAT* I WAS SQUEEZING.

EACH TIME I PUNCHED THE HEAVY BAG, I WAS PULPING YOUR *FACE.*

"I TAPED HEADLINES ABOUT YOU ON MY WALLS, FEEDING MY HATRED, KNOWING THAT *I* COULDN'T GET A STORY EVEN ON THE *BACK PAGE* OF ANY RESPECTABLE PAPER.

"UNTIL, FINALLY, THE PAIN BECAME UNBEARABLE--

ALMOST THERE...!

"-- AND I DECIDED TO END IT. *ALL*. BUT I WAS RAISED CATHOLIC, AND SUICIDE IS A *MORTAL* SIN. SO I WANDERED FROM CHURCH TO SHADOWED CHURCH, PRAYING FOR FORGIVENESS. THEN, AT *OUR LADY OF SAINTS*, SOMETHING... *ODD* HAPPENED.

"A SHADOW MOVED. CARESSED ME.

" I WAS JOINED.

BUT THIS WAS A SHADOW FILLED WITH *LIGHT*. IT CLARIFIED MY ANGUISH, FOCUSED MY PURPOSE. ITS *HATRED* FOR YOU MATCHED MY OWN.

IT KNEW WHO YOU WERE. AND IT HAD POWER. OH, *SUCH* POWER!

WE FOUND THE WOMAN FIRST. LATER, WE FOUND YOUR EMPTY APARTMENT. YOU WERE RUNNING FROM US.

"BUT THE SHADOW KNEW YOU WELL, KNEW YOU'D *HAVE* TO LEARN WHO WE WERE. SO WE WENT 'TROLLING,' USING OURSELVES AS A LURE. AND APPARENTLY, THE BAIT -- "

NOW!

I THINK I'M IN TROUBLE! ¿OONF?

THE ALIEN WASN'T REALLY *KILLED* BY THOSE BELLS! MUST'VE JUST DISSIPATED OUT OF PAIN! OR... REJECTION!

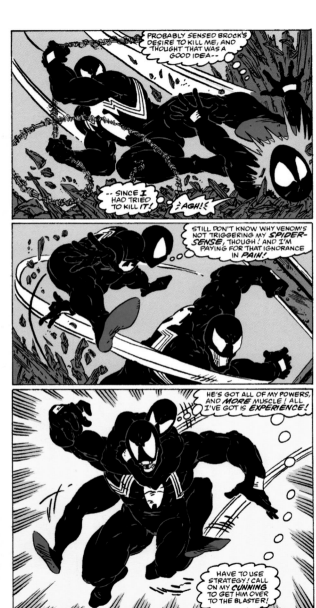

PROBABLY SENSED BROCK'S DESIRE TO KILL ME, AND THOUGHT THAT WAS A GOOD IDEA--

-- SINCE *I* HAD TRIED TO KILL *IT!*

¿AGH!¿

STILL DON'T KNOW WHY VENOM'S NOT TRIGGERING MY *SPIDER-SENSE*, THOUGH! AND I'M PAYING FOR THAT IGNORANCE IN *PAIN!*

HE'S GOT ALL OF MY POWERS, AND *MORE* MUSCLE! ALL I'VE GOT IS *EXPERIENCE!*

HAVE TO USE STRATEGY! CALL ON MY *CUNNING* TO GET HIM OVER TO THE BLASTER!

WHAUGH

SO MUCH...

...FOR FINESSE!

WHROK

NOW, YOU SON OF A--!

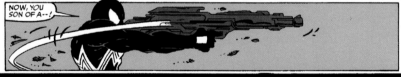

YIIIIIINNNEEGH!

I DON'T GET IT! WHEN MR. FANTASTIC USED THE BLASTER ON *ME*, THE SYMBIOTE WAS DRIVEN *AWAY*!

BUT IT'S ONLY *PULLING* AWAY FROM BROCK! WHY ISN'T IT *DETACHING*? UNLESS--

-- IT *CAN'T*? IT MUST HAVE COMPLETELY *BONDED* WITH HIS *BODY*! THAT'S WHY HE ISN'T TRIGGERING MY SPIDER-SENSE! THE *ALIEN* NEVER TRIPPED IT--

-- AND NOW HE *IS* THE ALIEN!

WHICH MEANS THAT IF I KILL *IT*...

...I'LL KILL *BROCK*!

DON'T KNOW IF I COULD TAKE A *HUMAN* LIFE EVEN TO SAVE MY OWN! AND AFTER THAT BEATING I TOOK, I DON'T HAVE MUCH *FIGHT* LEFT!

I'D BETTER REGROUP, THINK UP A NEW *PLAN*--!

LEAVING?

UH-UH.

PLIP

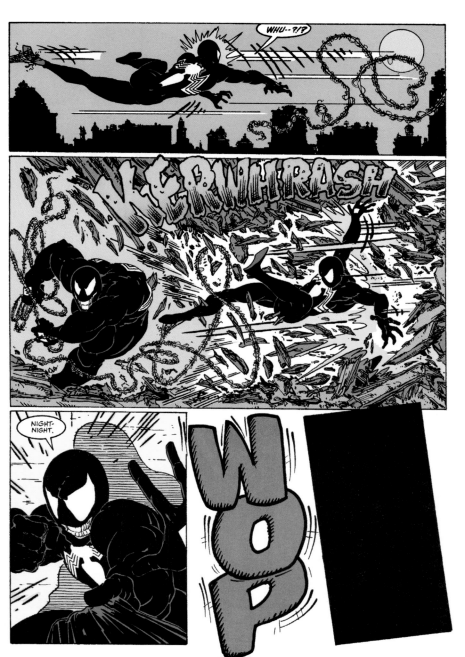

UUUUUHH...

WELCOME BACK TO THE LAND OF THE LIVING, SPIDER-MAN! WHAT A PITY YOUR STAY WILL BE SUCH A *SHORT* ONE!

WHA-- *LORD!*

APROPOS SENTIMENTS, CONSIDERING THE CIRCUM- STANCES.

JUST AS MY ALTERED *GARB* IS APPROPRIATE. AFTER ALL, WE ARE, IN A MANNER OF *SPEAKING,* ABOUT TO *EXORCISE--*

--A *DEMON!*

HIH HEEE HA HA HA!

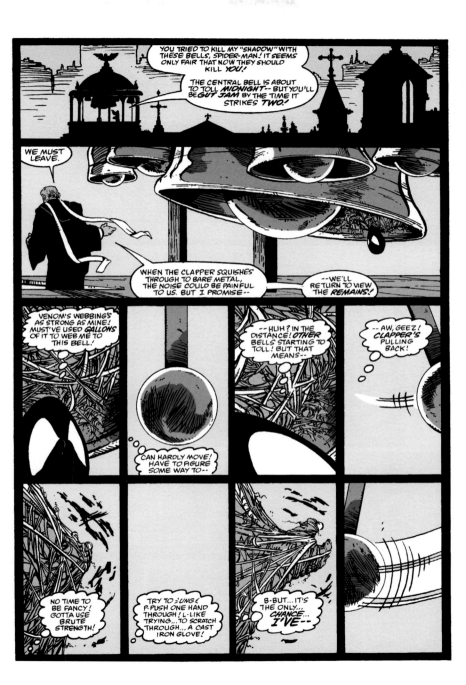

≥WHEW≥

STOPPED IT ONCE. BUT HOW MANY TIMES CAN I PULL THAT STUNT--

--BEFORE THE BONES IN MY HAND ARE CRUSHED TO *POWDER*?

STRANGE. WE SHOULD HAVE HEARD SOMETHING BY NOW.

A CRUNCH, A SCREAM... *SOMETHING!*

≥AGH!≥

NOW OR NEVER! WON'T BE ABLE TO STOP IT AGAIN!

MAYBE *I* DON'T HAVE THE STRENGTH TO PULL MYSELF FROM THIS WEBBING IN TIME, BUT I'LL BET MY GOOD RIGHT ARM THAT THE AUTOMATED BELL-RINGING *MACHINERY--*

THINK, SPIDEY! HOW CAN YOU *FIGHT* THIS GUY? HE HAS THE SAME POWERS AS YOU, THE SAME WEBBING, THE SAME-- WAIT! HE *DOESN'T* HAVE THE SAME WEBBING!

WHEN *I* WORE THE ALIEN SUIT, I NEVER NEEDED WEBBING CARTRIDGES! NEVER EVEN KNEW WHERE THE WEBBING *CAME* FROM!

AND I REMEMBER *PUMA* SAYING THE WEBBING WAS ORGANIC! *

THAT COULD MEAN IT'S MADE OF THE ALIEN'S OWN *SUB-STANCE,* THAT HE REGENERATES IT OVER TIME! AND *THAT* COULD BE MY KEY--

KRRIK

* IN *AMAZING SPIDER-MAN #* 258-- J.S.

--TO *SURVIVAL!*

BLONG

THWOK

PLIP

BROCK'S ALIVE--AND SO'S THE ALIEN. THOUGH IT HASN'T REGENERATED ENOUGH OF ITS MASS TO BE A *THREAT* YET.

I'LL NEED TO CONTAIN THEM BOTH, BUT THAT'LL HAVE TO WAIT. NOW--

--IF ONLY I CAN REMEMBER MARY JANE'S *CALLING CARD* NUMBER!

SOON... BEDFORD TOWERS? THIS IS MR. PARKER FROM 8-C. WE JUST MOVED IN AND DON'T HAVE A PHONE YET. COULD YOU POSSIBLY PASS A MESSAGE ALONG TO MY WIFE?

BE MY PLEASURE, SIR. WHAT'S THE GLAD WORD?

SECURITY

JUST TELL HER I HAD TO PHOTO-GRAPH A NEWS STORY, THAT I'LL BE HOME SOON, AND MOST OF ALL...TELL HER I'M *OKAY.*

AND SO, SOME TIME LATER AT *FOUR FREEDOMS PLAZA--*

--HOME OF THE LEGENDARY *FANTASTIC FOUR*--

-- CURRENT TEAM LEADER *BENJAMIN GRIMM* COMPLETES IMPROVISED SECURITY ARRANGE-MENTS...

I'VE BEEN ON THE HORN WITH MR. FANTASTIC, AN' HE SAYS THE *SONICS* BEIN' PIPED INTA THIS CYLINDER SHOULD KEEP *VENOM* NICE AN' DOCILE. LEASTWAYS--

--TILL A SPECIAL CELL CAN BE BUILT FOR 'IM AT *THE VAULT,* THAT GOVERNMENT SUPER-PRISON OUT IN THE ROCKIES.'

HEY, NO PROBLEM. ONLY NEXT TIME, TRY TA BRING YER LOONIES IN A LITTLE *EARLIER,* WILL YA? ⸎YAWN⸎

I REALLY APPRECIATE THIS, BEN.

SPIDER-MAN MAKES THE TRIP TO THE BEDFORD TOWERS CAREFULLY, FAVORING HIS LEFT ARM.

AND ONCE THERE, AFTER HIS TALE HAS BEEN TOLD...

WHAT'S WRONG, MJ? YOU SEEM AWFULLY... *DISTANT.*

I *SAID* I WAS SORRY. I DID WHAT I FELT I *HAD* TO DO.

I UNDERSTAND, PETER. REALLY. AND I'M GLAD YOU'RE OKAY.

THEN WHY THE ICEBOX TREATMENT? IS IT BECAUSE I HAVE TO GO RIGHT BACK *OUT* AGAIN?

SWEETHEART, IF I DON'T SHOW UP AT *THE BUGLE* WITH PHOTOGRAPHS OF *SOMETHING* TOMORROW, ROBBIE AND THE OTHERS' WILL GET SUSPICIOUS ABOUT WHY I DISAPPEARED FROM THE MOVE PARTY.' I HAVE TO--

I KNOW!

I... I DIDN'T MEAN TO SNAP AT YOU, PETER. BUT YOU'RE RIGHT-- I AM UPSET, ONLY IT'S NOT BECAUSE OF YOU. IT'S BECAUSE OF... WELL...

...THAT!

AFTER ALL WE'VE BOTH BEEN THROUGH, I DON'T THINK I'LL EVER FEEL COMFORTABLE AROUND THAT COSTUME.

YEAH, I KNOW WHAT YOU MEAN.

WEARING THE SAME OUTFIT AS A HOMICIDAL MANIAC DOESN'T THRILL ME, EITHER!

AND SINCE IT'S IMPOSSIBLE TO GET VENOM'S SUIT AWAY FROM HIM--

--I GUESS I'LL JUST HAVE TO DO WITHOUT MINE.

'COURSE, SWINGING AROUND THE CITY IN MY WEB-SHOOTERS AND FRUIT-OF-THE-LOOMS ISN'T GOING TO DO WONDERS FOR MY IMAGE!

I HAVE AN IDEA ABOUT THAT, PETER.

I KNOW THIS ISN'T A REAL COSTUME, JUST A COMMERCIAL COPY YOU GOT WHEN YOU WERE IN GERMANY. * BUT RIGHT NOW--

--IT ALMOST SEEMS LIKE AN OLD FRIEND. WHAT DO YOU THINK?

* IN THE SPIDER-MAN VS. WOLVERINE SPECIAL:- J.S.

MARY JANE, I THINK--

--YOU'RE THE GREATEST!

A LINGERING KISS, A QUICK CHANGE OF CLOTHES, AND...

[184]